CATHOLICISM AND THE
PROGRESS OF SCIENCE

THE MACMILLAN COMPANY
NEW YORK · BOSTON · CHICAGO · DALLAS
ATLANTA · SAN FRANCISCO

MACMILLAN AND CO., Limited
LONDON · BOMBAY · CALCUTTA · MADRAS
MELBOURNE

THE MACMILLAN COMPANY
OF CANADA, Limited
TORONTO

CATHOLICISM
AND THE PROGRESS
OF SCIENCE

By William M. Agar, Ph.D.

New York · 1940

THE MACMILLAN COMPANY

Nihil obstat
Arthur J. Scanlan, S.T.D.
CENSOR LIBRORUM.

Imprimatur
✠ Francis J. Spellman, D.D.
ARCHBISHOP, New York.

New York, July 19, 1940.

PRINTED IN THE UNITED STATES OF AMERICA

215.
A

THE CHRISTENDOM SERIES

PREFACE

A VOLUMINOUS literature already exists dealing with the controversies that have occurred between religion and science. Many volumes treat particular controversies far more exhaustively than they can be dealt with here. But, while such studies are extremely valuable, they do not survey the whole subject or trace the sequence of events in such a way that the reader can follow the development of science and understand the trends of thought at the times when controversies occurred.

The present volume outlines the history of science from its inception and emphasizes the continuity of development as well as the changing modes of thought which mark separate periods of history. It attempts also to describe past controversies impartially, and to show that there was sufficient knowledge at the time of each dispute to have enabled intelligent and dispassionate men to avoid it.

Such a general statement is easy to make and equally difficult to prove. Nevertheless, if unnecessary conflicts are to be avoided in the present and future, its full implications must be grasped. Passion, fear, and ignorance on both sides have displaced reason in the past and they can do so just as readily today. Past controversies teach us that we must know the limits and the possibilities of science as well as the true teachings of the Church in order to avoid many disputes and to resolve those few which will inevitably arise. The present volume is devoted to that end.

But much more is needed. It is essential to know how knowledge can be gained, what is fact and what is theory, and what fundamental verities can be agreed upon, before it becomes possible to judge modern disputes reasonably. Lack of space forbids such a discussion in these pages. Hence an analysis of the necessary philosophic background and of the meaning and value of the scientific method is reserved to a second volume that will presently appear in this series.

The reader of this volume should have in mind at the outset, however, the distinction between the scientific theory of evolution and evolution as a philosophy. As later explained, the scientific theory is that life has developed from life with change and specialization from simple beginnings up to the manifold types now existing. The Catholic view of man as a compound of spiritual soul and material body coupled with the fact that the life principal in animals is essentially material, precludes the acceptance of the evolution of man *as a whole* from animal life. Otherwise this theory contains nothing contrary to the Catholic view.

Evolution, as a philosophy, supposes that matter has evolved itself from primitive chaos into all of its existing stages of perfection including man's mind and soul.

Preface

This idea assumes that effects can be more perfect than their efficient causes. It makes no distinction between Creator and creature and leads, consequently, into various forms of pantheism. It is the background out of which philosophic naturalism has arisen and is inadmissible by Catholics or by any believers in revealed religion.

The writer is indebted to the *Commonweal* for permission to use material previously published in its pages. He wishes also to express his gratitude to Rev. Ninian MacDonald, O.S.B., Rev. Quitman Beckley, O.P., Rev. Gerald G. Walsh, S.J., Professor Carlton Hayes, Professor Ross Hoffman, Herbert Agar, and Xavier Prum, who have read and criticized the manuscript and made many valuable suggestions.

CONTENTS

CHAPTER I

THE DEVELOPMENT OF SCIENCE

SCIENCE is defined as classified knowledge of natural phenomena and the relationships between them. The history of the growth of this knowledge is long and complicated and it is not the purpose of this volume to develop it exhaustively. There are, however, certain salient facts which must be emphasized before embarking upon a discussion of the controversies which have occurred between science and religion, and the present chapter reviews the general development of science with that in view.

It is necessary to realize, first, that science had developed to considerable heights in classical antiquity but had decayed with the growing power of the Roman Empire and was almost eclipsed at its fall; second, that the Fathers of the Christian Church were leaders in expounding cosmological doctrine, in pointing out that some passages of Genesis were not meant to be literal in their significance, and in laying the foundation for accord between Christianity and science; third, that science was mingled with magic left over from pagan days; fourth, that when science began to be studied again in Europe after the introduction of the writings of Aristotle and of other Greeks through the Arabian schools, the leading scholastic philosophers were its chief proponents and advocated the use of the scientific method; fifth, that the transition from medieval to modern science was more gradual and normal than historians, until recently, have been wont to picture it.

I. SCIENCE IN ANCIENT PAGAN TIMES

The origin of science is forever lost beyond the dim beginnings of recorded history. Primitive man must, perforce, have been a keen observer of nature and possessed of considerable mechanical skill and a knowledge of practical science. Anyone who doubts this need only try to fashion the rudest stone implements and then turn his hand to chipping spear heads of flint and other fine-grained stones in order to be convinced. Before the dawn of history man knew how to make fire by friction, how to cook with fire, which herbs and cereals were good to eat, which plants were poisonous. He invented the wheel, fashioned boats, melted and cast metal, and knew how to till and manage the land so as to increase nature's fertility. But, so far as we know, these accomplishments were solely the fruits of experience and were not connected in a body of knowledge by means of the rational explanations which make science what it is today.

A more advanced type of practical science flourished in early Egypt, in Babylon, Chaldea, and China. The Egyptians and Babylonians mapped the sky and learned many things that required persistent and accurate observation coupled with a certain power of abstraction, but explanations were not forthcoming because natural phenomena were still regarded as caused by capricious deities who must be propitiated by various rites.

The Greeks of the early Attic period (approximately 500 to 400 B.C.) were the first, so far as we know, to place science on a rational basis. They found the world ascribing everything that happened to the manipulations of good and bad deities and semi-human heroes; they left it with a well developed notion of natural cause and effect and the first concept of scientific law. The great names of that period still rank at the top in the history of human thought: Pythagoras, Thales, Anaxagoras, Democritus, Hippocrates, the philosophers Socrates and Plato, and finally Aristotle (384–322 B.C.). These not only handed down many of the greatest thoughts that the human mind has produced, but also developed methods of thought and analysis which could be used by their successors; so that this period was followed shortly by a still greater outburst of scientific genius centering about the schools and libraries of Alexandria and lasting for more than four hundred years. Euclid, Eristratus, Archimedes, Aristarchus, Eratosthenes, Hipparchus, and Hero, added to the foundations of modern physical, astronomical, and medical sciences and advanced far in their understanding of natural law. But learning was confined to relatively few men and we cannot think of the public as being enlightened scientifically. Though we do not know exactly how deep this knowledge sank into the popular consciousness, it appears that most men were still steeped in magic and mythology.

There are two names in the above list which we must note particularly, Aristarchus (250 B.C.) and Hipparchus (160–125 B.C.), for these were the precursors of a dispute which reached its climax over seventeen hundred years later. Aristarchus, if not the first to mention it, at least developed the heliocentric theory of the solar system and showed that the Earth moved around the Sun in an orbit which he considered circular. Eratosthenes, his immediate successor, followed him in this and proved the spheroidal form of the Earth to the satisfaction of learned men. Unfortunately, Hipparchus held firmly to the idea that the Earth was immovable and established the geocentric theory, with the Earth at the center of the heavens and all the other bodies revolving around it, as an accepted fact of science. Hipparchus was known in his day as an accurate observer and his truly remarkable influence prevented the correct concept of the relation of the Sun to the Earth from taking hold. It is especially interesting to note that he and his followers believed in their own theory in large part because it gave a common-sense explanation of the rising and setting of the Sun as well as of the motions of the stars. Right at the beginning the matter-of-fact observer with an unimaginative mind came in contact with an imaginative scientist. The matter-of-fact man won out with his common-sense explanation and the truth was buried for seventeen hundred years.

The Development of Science

Much later, in the second century A.D., Claudius Ptolemy, one of the last of the scientific Alexandrians, popularized and developed the geocentric theory still further, so that it became known as the Ptolemaic Theory of the solar system and continued to dominate cosmologic thought until the time of Copernicus and Galileo.

The genius of the Romans was not directed along scientific lines, as can be seen from the fact that only four names, Pliny, Strabo, Galen, and Ptolemy stand out during the period of the Roman Empire. Of the four only Pliny and Strabo were Romans.

Pliny was primarily a compiler; his great work, *Natural History,* was published in 77 A.D. in thirty-seven volumes. This is essentially an encyclopedia of ancient knowledge and contains nearly as much misinformation as information. It shows more credulity than scientific scepticism and is full of magic formulas and other signs of belief in demons and occult powers.

Strabo was a geographer who did some original work but was above all a collator of facts. Galen, the great physician, who eclipsed all the ancients save only Hippocrates and made real contributions to scientific knowledge and method, was a Greek. Ptolemy, whose *Almagest* was well known in Europe throughout the Middle Ages and whose *Geography* was first translated into Latin near the opening of the fifteenth century, was born and lived in Egypt. Besides his work on astronomy, the importance of which was indicated above, he developed the methods of trigonometry, ad-

5

vanced cartography by perfecting a means of project-
ing spherical surfaces on a flat map, and apparently
dealt successfully with many problems in optics, including the relation of the eye to light, mirrors, and refrac-
tion. He used exact mathematical and scientific methods,
yet he sanctioned the art of astrology, believing that a
force is diffused from the heavens over all things on
the Earth.

Plutarch, a learned pagan, wrote many books which
are full of bits of pseudo-science, divination, and magic.
He ridiculed the notion of the antipodes and the idea
that the Earth is spherical. Together with the rest of
the Neo-Platonists he believed firmly that both the motions of the heavenly bodies and emanations from them
affect things upon the Earth. In other words, pagan
antiquity, to its dying day, was steeped in magic, given
to divination and to belief in astrology and alchemy.
This belief was handed on to the early Christians and,
as history shows, was extremely difficult to eradicate.

2. Science and the Christian Fathers

We frequently fail to realize that as Christianity
came out of the East and into the West, it opened the
door to many long-hidden Eastern beliefs that well-
nigh overwhelmed it in the first two hundred years of
its existence. Chesterton puts it vividly in the following
words: "When the Faith first emerged into the world,
the very first thing that happened to it was that it was
caught in a sort of swarm of mystical and metaphysical
sects, mostly out of the East; like one lonely golden bee

6

caught in a swarm of wasps. . . . . Or, to vary
the metaphor, when this movement or some other movement pierced the dyke between the east and west and
brought more mystical ideas into Europe, it brought
with it a whole flood of other mystical ideas besides its
own, most of them ascetical and nearly all of them
pessimistic. They nearly flooded and overwhelmed the
purely Christian element." [1]

One of the chief difficulties seems to have been that
of separating the idea of Christ's miracles, in the popular mind, from the firmly embedded ideas of magic.
Origen was one of the first to attempt it and, though
himself a firm believer in the Scriptures, was driven
more and more towards allegory in his interpretation.
Lactantius sharply differentiated miracles from magic
but took what was more nearly an anti-scientific stand
than any others. He has often been quoted because of
the ridicule he heaped upon the idea of the antipodes
and the spherical form of the Earth. But we have seen
that even a scientific pagan could do this.

St. Augustine, who was so important an authority on
so many things, St. Basil, and St. Gregory of Nyssa
occupied themselves at length with the exact meaning
and proper interpretation of the book of Genesis. These
men were not scientists in the accepted meaning of the
term but they were conversant with the science of their
day. St. Augustine's theory of knowledge is idealistic
as a whole but he did claim that knowledge of intelligible objects gained through the senses was *one* of the

[1] G. K. Chesterton, *The Everlasting Man*, N. Y., 1926, p. 275.

two methods of knowing, and he spent long years of his life opposing the literal interpretation of Scripture in matters pertaining to natural history. He also constructed his own cosmologic theories which we shall presently have reason to discuss.

According to Dorlodot, the *Homilies* of St. Basil on the Hexaëmeron, delivered in the cathedral of Caesarea in Cappodocia in the latter part of the fourth century, aroused a storm of criticism because he abandoned the early teaching and defended the literal interpretation of the meaning of the *days* in Genesis. St. Gregory of Nyssa, his brother, claimed that St. Basil's teaching was not properly understood; that in the cases complained of he had descended, as a preacher, to the level of his audience. Actually it appears that St. Basil's defence of the view that Genesis taught a real succession of actual days, represented a reaction against the extreme views of the Alexandrian school, notably those of Origen, which pictured the Bible as largely allegorical.[2]

St. Gregory himself developed a theory of natural evolution or unfolding of the world which formally denied special intervention by God after the great act of Creation, but he attempted to adapt his explanation to the order of succession of six days. St. Augustine, after a long study of the problem, went further than any of the others, and reached the conclusion that formless matter was originally created out of nothing but

[2] Henri de Dorlodot, *Darwinism and Catholic Thought*, N. Y., 1923, pp. 67–68.

8

that the complexities of living matter were only *virtually* created at the beginning and that they appeared successively at the proper time—they were present at the beginning *in their causes only*. He rejected any attempt at literalness and wrote that "the exposition according to the order of the days has only the appearance of history," for God was not placed in a certain spot so that it would be evening for Him when the light left there. He wrote further: "Remember that God, wishing to teach men that the universe is the work of His might, had to express Himself after the ordinary manner of men in order to be understood by them. That is why He spoke according to the appearances and according to the opinions of those to whom the creation narrative was immediately addressed." As he also pointed out, the argument that the commandment, "Remember thou keep holy the Sabbath Day," is based upon the actual repose of God who had rested on the seventh day, breaks down when we stop and think, for God did not work and rest in time.

The strength of St. Augustine's position on scientific matters is best summarized in a quotation from St. Thomas Aquinas: "In the institution of nature we do not look for miracles, but for the laws of nature, as Augustine said." St. Augustine was a philosopher and a theologian, rather than a scientist, and yet he warned his contemporaries: "Often, in connection with the Earth and the heavens, or other elements of this world, the movement, circuit, or still more the magnitude of the stars and of the intervals separating them, or else in

9

connection with eclipses of the sun and of the moon, the cycle of years and of times, the exact nature of animals, fruits, rocks, and many other similar things, it happens that a man who is not a Christian possesses a knowledge which is so profound that it is guaranteed by certain calculation, or even by experience. Now, here is a thing which is too disgraceful, too disastrous, and from which we must, above all, guard ourselves: a Christian speaks on all these subjects; he thinks that he speaks of them according to our Holy Scriptures; yet every unbeliever may hear him rambling so much that in the presence of such great errors the unbeliever cannot help laughing. And the real evil is not that a man is subjected to derision because of his error, but it is that to profane eyes our authors (that is to say, the sacred authors) are regarded as having had such thoughts; and are also exposed to blame and scorn on the score of ignorance, to the greatest possible misfortune of people whom we wish to save." [3] The story of controversies between Christianity and science would have been quite different if this advice had been followed.

3. SCIENCE IN THE MIDDLE AGES

Shortly after St. Augustine's time the Western Empire crumbled and Europe was occupied for several centuries in civilizing successive hordes of barbarians that overwhelmed it. Science was eclipsed, though it remained alive in the East and within a generation

[3] *De Genesi ad Literam,* Liber I, Cap. XIX. Translation as given in Dorlodot, *op. cit.,* p. 62.

after the death of Mohammed (632 A.D.) began to flourish among the Arabs and was brought back into Europe by them. Physics, astronomy, and medicine were all advanced. The Arabic numerals, probably borrowed from the Hindus, and the decimal system were introduced; trigonometry was developed, and many new chemical compounds, particularly metallic compounds and acids were discovered and used. Many drugs were used in medicine, and medical schools and hospitals grew both in the East and in the West.

Even during the lowest ebb in the fifth and sixth centuries when medicine was probably more largely magic than it had been before, some measure of scientific medicine and the important place of physicians in the community were retained.

"The laws of the German Kingdoms," writes Lynn Thorndike, "the allusions of contemporary chroniclers and men of letters, the advice of Gregory the Great to a sick archbishop to seek medical assistance, and many other bits of evidence show that physicians were fairly numerous and in good repute, and that medieval Christians at no time depended entirely upon the healing virtues of relics of the Saints or other miraculous powers credited to the Church or divine answer to prayer." [4]

The early Christians appear to have built the first hospitals though these were soon eclipsed in size, if not in zeal, by those constructed by the Arabs all the way

[4] Lynn Thorndike, *A History of Magic and Experimental Science*, N. Y. Macmillan, 1923, Vol. I, p. 593.

from Samarkand to Spain. By 1000 A.D., the famous Christian medical school at Salerno, Italy, was already flourishing, and others developed not long afterwards.

The date of origin and the source of the mariners' compass are difficult to place accurately, but it appears to have been developed in Europe during the eleventh or early twelfth centuries, and knowledge of navigation advanced rapidly after that.

We do not know as much about the science of the early Middle Ages as we would like. There is a scarcity of manuscripts dating from that period, explainable in part at least by the fact that it was necessary to copy each one by hand. Once a manuscript was superseded by a new one, it was no longer copied and the existing copies wore out or were lost.[5] Probably there was more scientific knowledge than we have record of, but even if this assumption be true, such knowledge seems to have been confined to relatively few men and it was strangely mixed with magic. The early Middle Ages, sometimes called the "dark ages," were certainly not a time of scientific experiment. Theologians were busy determining the boundaries of revelation and the meaning of the Scriptures, and they hesitated to accept ideas which were not easily seen to agree with the Scriptures. They were overly cautious perhaps, but they did not interfere with the development of science in any positive way.

Roger Bacon (1214–1294), at the height of the

[5] Henry Smith Williams, *A History of Science*, N. Y., 1904, Vol. II, p. 8.

Middle Ages properly so called, has been represented by many writers as the real originator of the scientific method, as a man who was obliged to overcome all sorts of opposition in order to advance the cause of experimental science. Lynn Thorndike's scholarly contention that Bacon's work proves conclusively that the germs of scientific thought were everywhere around him seems much more plausible and fruitful.[6] For, though Bacon was a boastful man, he made no such claims to originality as many writers have ascribed to him. Bacon was primarily a critic of the existing knowledge and methods of teaching. He worked hard and wrote many textbooks before becoming a Franciscan friar. His retirement from active work for a long period together with his order's attempt to make him carry out the ordinary duties of a friar have given rise to the statements that he was persecuted and prevented from working in his beloved science. Actually, this partial retirement was caused by ill health. The Pope of the time, apparently anxious to discover what remedies Bacon had to offer for the conditions which he criticized, called for his work in 1266 and repeatedly urged him to go on with his writing. Spurred in this way, Bacon produced the *Opus Majus* and his other works. His major work is a compendium but, as Thorndike observes, it is an extraordinary book and certainly reflects the thought of the day, though it did little to advance experimental science, save perhaps by precept.

Bacon's contemporary, St. Albertus Magnus (about

[6] Thorndike, op. cit., Vol. II, pp. 616–689.

1193–1286), was certainly the greatest scientist of the age and the most original thinker. From his own observation, he added much to the teaching of Aristotle and other authorities. He had a real desire for concrete knowledge and did some crude though purposive experimentation. His writings include volumes on zoölogy, entomology, botany, chemistry, physics, and astronomy. Naturally, they contain much that sounds strange to us, but the results attained were important and they prove his powers of observation, classification, and inference; they show that he practiced what we now call the scientific method.

St. Albertus Magnus is credited with having anticipated Thomas Graham's discovery and use of the methods of dyalisis (the separation and purification of materials in solution by means of semi-permeable membranes), and his strong advocacy of the ancient idea that the Earth was a sphere had much to do with hastening the voyages of discovery later initiated by Columbus, for both Columbus and Copernicus possessed St. Albert's works and annotated sets of these are still preserved full of their user's notes. Furthermore, some of St. Albert's cosmological suggestions seem clearly to have influenced Copernicus' thought, as they did Kepler's still later.

The scholastic philosophers of the thirteenth century, particularly St. Albertus Magnus and St. Thomas Aquinas, based their thinking on the evidence of the senses and believed that it was necessary to prove by reason the need for faith, and to show that God must exist before discussing His attributes. They remained faithful to the spirit of Christian naturalism established by St. Augustine; that is, they looked for natural explanations of natural events and avoided calling on miracles. St. Thomas stated clearly that to the ultimate truth religion and science were approaches which must be developed side by side and kept in harmony with each other. Their whole mode of thought was rational and logical and had place in it for knowledge of all kinds.

But, in spite of all this, belief in astrology, that is in the effect of the heavens upon the affairs of men, persisted. Duns Scotus (1308), who held that "Knowledge obtained through the senses and by experimental verification of the natural existence of things is the basis and source of all other forms of knowledge," was fully as favorable to astrology as were St. Albertus Magnus and St. Thomas Aquinas. Divining, interpretation of dreams, black magic, and some of the work of the alchemists were repeatedly frowned upon, though they were no more extinguished than are various superstitions today; but astrology was generally deemed true. Agostino Trionfo (1243–1328) wrote to Pope Clement V against diviners and dreamers and warned him that the Apostolic See should not listen to prophets of things future and occult. He censured the Clergy who encouraged superstition, yet he firmly believed in the effect of the stars and planets on man's plans, writing that an astrologer would sin if he allowed a client to sail when the Sun was in an unfavorable sign which portended a dangerous storm. These statements, however, cannot be taken as meaning that stellar influences were compelling, since St. Thomas in particular, and others as well, repeatedly stated that the will of man is free. His choice could be influenced but his actions were ultimately determined by his own will.

Pope John XXII, reigning from 1316 to 1334, was forced to take notice of the prevalence of magical arts and of the civil and ecclesiastical court trials that resulted therefrom. His bull, *Super Illius Specula,* was a fulmination against magic and it excommunicated all offenders. The same Pope, as we shall recall later, issued a decretal against the alchemists which was intended to prevent the practice of counterfeiting. It is true also, throughout the Middle Ages, as well as in the earlier pagan times, that alchemy had less standing than astrology among educated people, and many of its practices were frowned upon; yet, in so far as the belief persisted that it was possible to obtain true silver and gold from base metals, it was considered perfectly legal to sell the product as such.

4. SCIENCE AND THE TRANSITION TO MODERN TIMES

From the fourteenth century on, there was a deterioration of scholastic thought. The universities ceased their search for new knowledge and became centers where dialectic was studied for its own sake and where argumentation was interminable and over-elaborated. The pure intellectuality of the Thomistic system weakened before the criticism of those who imagined that many of the problems which it posed could not be solved at all. By the fifteenth century the tide set definitely against the rationalism of the early leaders; many turned away from philosophy entirely.

Shortly afterwards the Protestant Reformation occurred, new ideas and new problems rose on all sides, and decadent scholasticism was too weak or too blind to recognize the value of these new ideas and to incorporate them. Furthermore, both Catholics and Protestants had come, by the sixteenth century, to regard the Bible as a chief arbiter in all matters of natural knowledge with the inevitable result so clearly foretold by St. Augustine, namely that the Bible as a whole was brought into disrepute. Thus the revival and extension of scientific knowledge began after reaction had already set in against philosophic speculation and against the old scholasticism and the old religion.

The history of the failure on the part of decadent scholasticism has been emphasized before, and we must now direct attention to the fact that it tells only half the story. New ideas and new methods never appear suddenly. They grow out of the past, and if we are to blame the scholastics of the fourteenth and fifteenth centuries for what occurred we must also recognize the basic contribution of the whole scholastic movement to the rise of modern science.

The foregoing cursory survey of the history of science must make one wonder what kept natural science from becoming important long before it did, and why it ever retreated from its early triumphs. The chief reason, it seems to us, was that ancient science was confined to a few great thinkers and never crept into the consciousness of the masses and that, even among the thinkers, it was strangely mixed with magic. Dissemination of knowledge was difficult then and when a period came which did not breed great scientists, a period in which men's energies were turned to other things, it was easy to lose what had been learned. On the other hand, modern science is more or less the property of all educated people and is the life work of multitudes of men, so that, between these two periods, great masses of men had to be taught to think and had to be trained in the methods of reasoning. From this point of view we see the late Middle Ages as the culmination of an age-long training of the human intellect and we can see the good emanating from the dying struggles of scholasticism, for the whole movement taught men exactness of thought and emphasized the need for clear and rational thinking. As Professor Whitehead has said: "But for science something more is wanted than a general sense of the order in things. It needs but a sentence to point out how the habit of definite exact thought was implanted in the European mind by the long dominance of scholastic divinity. The habit remained after the philosophy had been repudiated, the priceless habit of looking for an exact point and sticking to it when found." Whitehead goes on to add that "the inexpugnable belief that every detailed occurrence can be correlated with its antecedents in a perfectly definite manner, exemplifying general principles," is the only thing that makes the incredible labors of scientists worth-while, and that the instinctive conviction "that there is a secret, a secret which can be unveiled," is the motive power of research. We must remember that these thinkers of the Middle Ages in Europe who explored the realms of thought and insisted on the rationality of God and His nature, are the immediate precursors in time and in place of the great age of science, whereas the mystics of the East who referred natural phenomena to an inscrutable force or to the "fiat of an irrational despot" gave rise to nothing of the sort. So does Professor Whitehead reach the conclusion "that the faith in the possibility of science, generated antecedently to the development of modern scientific theory, is an unconscious derivative from medieval theology." [7]

This notion is unfamiliar to most scientists and philosophers today but, from a purely logical point of view, it furnishes a much more illuminating explanation of the development of science—giving it roots and a history—than does the time-worn picture of the Church suppressing science, at first successfully, then more and more vainly until the pent-up power of the new thought burst through and the suppressing force collapsed in fragments. The latter view totally disregards the facts of history as well as the work of so many of the early scientists who were Catholics and often priests and bishops.

Those who do see the truth in this admit the useful-

[7] A. N. Whitehead, *Science and the Modern World*, N. Y., 1926, pp. 17–19.

ness of the training but are apt to claim that, when science did develop, the old learning was no longer needed. They regard it, in other words, as they do any discarded scientific theory which served a definite purpose in its time by pointing the way to newer truth, but has now only a historical value.

There were, however, many foreshadowings of the approaching age of science to be seen in the fourteenth and fifteenth centuries. As historical scholars come to know these centuries better, the tendency to pick out a few great men and play them up as moderns, born before their time, is giving way before the fuller realization of the historical continuity that connects the events of the thirteenth with those of the sixteenth century. As Professor Thorndike says, "Candid inquirers are becoming increasingly convinced that the true Renaissance occurred in the twelfth century rather than in the fifteenth." [8] He also claims that there was a definite regression from the general productiveness of the twelfth and thirteenth centuries and attributes it to the effects of the Hundred Years' War, to the sinister development of absolution in the despotisms of the Italian cities, the centralization of the governing power in France in the hands of the King, and, not least, to the Black Death of 1348 and the recurrent visitations of the same plague. Another factor was the development of humanism and the reaction against the immediate past which gave a ready excuse for men to seek

[8] Lynn Thorndike, *Science and Thought in the Fifteenth Century*, N. Y., 1929, Introduction.

for leisure and cultured ease rather than to train their minds to battle with the intricacies of logic and the difficulty of producing new ideas.

During the fourteenth and fifteenth centuries systematic dissection was practiced, great advances were made in knowledge of how to control infection, leprosy declined markedly, a mercury salve for syphilis was manufactured, and plastic surgery was developed to a high degree of proficiency by the Brancas, father and son.

These centuries also witnessed the invention of printing, the development of the ship's rudder and many other improvements necessitated by the invention of the mariner's compass which permitted navigation in the open sea. Artillery and firearms were developed after the invention of gunpowder which dated from the thirteenth century. The first blast furnace was fired and resulted in great progress in iron working. The mechanical clocks of the fourteenth century were marvelous instruments representing the movements of the heavenly bodies and the clockmakers were called upon to help develop machines of all kinds. James (about 1290–1359) and John de Dondis (1318–1389) developed one of the best and most complicated of these mechanical clocks which marked the course of the planets as well as the hours. They both taught medicine, were interested in astronomy and wrote concerning the hot mineral springs near Padua.

This was also an age of discovery second, perhaps, only to the age that followed. China, Asia, North

Africa across the Sahara and even beyond the equator, were well known and frequently visited. The beginning of westward exploration revealed the Canary Islands and the Azores and, in 1455, the Cape Verde Islands were discovered. Advances were made in medicine, mathematics, calendar reform, astronomical tables, and in legal thought and writing. Richard Suiseth's *Calculations,* which were mathematical and logical in character, represent, according to Professor Thorndike, a significant type of exposition prevalent at that time. To quote, "They [The Calculations] appear as the leading model of a great mass of writing during the closing middle ages devoted to the intensity and remission or latitude of forms, to uniformity and difformity, the proportions of velocities, reaction, and maximum and minimum, and kindred topics and concepts. This involved and subtle scholastic discussion of problems which were physical and mathematical as well as exercises in logic became anathema and an object of loathing to the tired humanists of the so-called Italian Renaissance and to those who lightly praised folly and preached reform beyond the Alps. Few modern scholars have had time and patience to try to puzzle it out. But although to a superficial view it appears to have been discarded then and neglected since, one suspects that in reality it was laying the foundation for the later development of the mathematical method in physical science; that it was striving to express in words and arguments what was later put much more clearly, forcibly, and conveniently into symbols and equations; that it was giving a first faulty theoretical expression to what was in time to be formulated upon a more concrete and exact basis of experimental physics." [9] It probably represented a necessary step in the further development of scientific thought.

At any rate the relative neglect of the scientific method, and the interminable wrangles of the philosophers of the fourteenth and fifteenth centuries which were the immediate cause of sixteenth century science's disregard of the old learning must not blind us to science's real dependence on the past. It is, in fact, this rejection of the past which caused modern science to forget its foundation on faith and intuition and which enabled it ultimately to become materialistic. The tendency of the times was to break away from previous methods and to start the development of knowledge all over again.

5. MODERN SCIENCE AND RELIGIOUS CONTROVERSY

We have now traced the development of science, its eclipse, and resurgence in the sixteenth century. We have seen that science developed in opposition to so much that went before partly because theologians hesitated to accept ideas which they could not easily accommodate to their particular interpretation of Scripture,

[9] Lynn Thorndike, op. cit., *A History of Magic* etc., Vol. III, p. 370.

but largely because the scientific method and outlook were new and men were not accustomed to such modes of thought. It is absolutely wrong, however, to regard this as the necessary outcome of the hold which Christianity had over men's minds, or to think of it as happening suddenly. When modern science began to develop, the real struggle was between the old science based on the authority of Aristotle and Ptolemy, and the new science based on observation—between the system of philosophy built up over fifteen centuries, and by then pretty well exhausted and sterile, and the new methods of gaining knowledge. It grew out of the very human fact that old ideas always seem best and that it is terribly hard to accept new truths when they demand a complete readjustment of processes of thought. It is also true that the old science had gradually become the basis of Christian cosmology and when it was attacked it appeared to many men that Christianity itself was being undermined.

Shortly after modern science got its start the conflict took on a more fundamental aspect and represented a divergence between those who considered the word of God and man's relation to God as the most important thing, and those who regarded human knowledge as self-sufficient. The first admittedly neglected a necessary means of gaining knowledge even about God and His way with the world; the second denied the most fundamental truth of all. The first held to the most important fact but succumbed to the counsel of fear as though they did not really believe that God had created nature as well as man's soul; the second came to think that if they knew how the world worked they also knew why it worked and where it came from.

The two points of view have slowly come together, though not without unedifying retreats on the part of theologians from ground that they had no business to occupy. But the fundamental divergence between the philosophies of naturalism and supernaturalism remains and the controversy has gradually centered around the nature of man and the problem of mind versus matter.

The history of the controversies between Christianity and modern science is partly the story of infringements by one side on the prerogatives of the other, and partly that of normal human resistance to new ideas which tend to upset traditional points of view. Scientists, on the one hand, have frequently reached conclusions, inimical to Christianity in matters far beyond the bounds dictated by science. Theologians, on their part, have resisted innovations because they did not see, at the time, how these could be reconciled with Scripture or revelation, and have sought safety in denying what was afterwards proved to be true.

This was not only harmful to religion in each case, but it helped the scientific movement to develop into a trend away from Christian philosophy and religion, and caused many to regard Catholicism as necessarily obscurantist. That is particularly unfortunate in view of the fact that it is the Church's duty to guard people against mistaken philosophical conceptions, whether advanced by science or under any other name, which will lead them into sterile ways of thought, if nothing worse. This will ever be a source of misunderstanding, since the world in general resents any claim in behalf of a higher authority. Hence it is doubly unfortunate when theologians bring their authority to bear on questions that can only be decided by the methods of science.

Much of modern science, as it developed from the sixteenth century, had a materialistic outlook, and between this and Christian philosophy there existed a very real and deep divergence, just as today a chasm separates the Christian viewpoint from the scepticism and pantheism towards which so many contemporary minds are tending. Because of this, bitter controversies can only be avoided by patience and a very real desire to understand the opposite viewpoint. Unfortunately, writers such as John W. Draper and Andrew D. White [10] have fanned the flames of controversy in a completely unjustifiable way by insisting on Christian opposition to the advance of science where history does not sanction their thesis. The books of such authors, though pretty thoroughly discredited, still have a con-

[10] Vide : *History of the Conflict between Religion and Science,* by John William Draper, N. Y., 1897, and *A History of the Warfare of Science with Theology in Christendom,* by Andrew D. White, 2 Vols., N. Y., 1897.

siderable market, and multitudes of people, ignorant of the truth, carry that notion of Christian opposition to science as a part of their mental outlook throughout life.

CHAPTER II

CONTROVERSIES ABOUT GEOGRAPHY AND ASTRONOMY

1. THE FORM OF THE EARTH AND THE EXISTENCE OF ANTIPODEANS

ONE of the earliest of the mistaken notions which Christianity is blamed for fostering is that the Earth is flat and no human beings can live on the other side. We have already mentioned several writers' views concerning the form of the Earth and we have seen that its sphericity was regarded as proved by many of the learned men of antiquity. Strabo even ridiculed Eratosthenes for his elaborate discussion of the point, since, as he said, it was so easy to prove that the Earth is a sphere. It is also certain that the concept of a flat Earth had few if any champions among the learned Christians of the Middle Ages.[1] On the other hand, we know that, throughout the days of the ascendency of pagan Greece and Rome, most of the ignorant regarded the Earth as just what it appeared to be—a flat surface with no inhabitants far beyond the boundaries of what was then known. This view was certainly the common one in the early centuries of the Christian era and persisted among the masses of the people into the sixteenth century. As

[1] Cf. Williams, op. cit., Vol. II, p. 52.

a consequence the Church is frequently accused of fostering it in direct opposition to enlightened opinion in order to stem the tide of material knowledge.

We must remember that the real proof that the Earth could be circumnavigated and that men lived on all sides of it had to wait until one of Magellan's ships accomplished the feat, in 1533, and brought back visual confirmation of the existence of antipodeans. This is now a part of our common heritage of knowledge but this was not so five hundred years ago and the existing concepts upon which the idea of the Earth's spherical form was based did not compel assent.

As a matter of fact there never was any opposition on the part of Christian apologists to the idea that the Earth was a sphere. Some were opposed, however, to the claim that men might exist on the other side because they did not understand how such inhabitants could have been descended from Adam, or how Christ could have saved them. We have already mentioned how Plutarch scoffed at the idea of the existence of the antipodes and, being a pagan, he certainly did not do so to advance the Christian point of view. So the Christian writers were not going against any generally accepted fact when they opposed the idea—the mistake they made was in supposing that the knowledge which they possessed gave them the right to an opinion on the matter.

St. Augustine, for instance, in his *City of God* (XVI, 9) wrote truly enough that those who affirm that men exist on the other side of the Earth, walking with their feet opposite to ours, do not do so from any evidence but merely conjecture that since the Earth is suspended in the concavity of the heavens there is as much room on the other side, which, therefore, cannot be void of human inhabitants. "They fail to notice," he said, "that, even should it be believed or demonstrated that the world is round or spherical in form, it does not follow that the part of the Earth opposite to ours is not completely covered with water, or that any conjectured dry land there should be inhabited by men." He claimed it was absurd to say that some men might have sailed around and established a race descended from Adam. Elsewhere St. Augustine states that the idea of the Earth's sphericity does not in any way conflict with Scripture and it is clear enough that he was anxious only to guard the unity of the race—which science labored mightily to uphold after it was shown how widely man was distributed. But it is difficult to understand, in the light of his warnings against just such things, how he could be so positive that men could not exist on the other side. In this case he seems to have gone against his own principles in denying the possibility of certain things simply because he could not see how they could be reconciled with the Scriptural account of Adam as the ancestor of man.

In 748 A.D., St. Boniface wrote to Pope St. Zachary invoking the latter's censure on Vergilius for holding, among other things, that "beneath the Earth, there was another world and other men, another Sun and Moon." The quoted expression is rather puzzling, but it was apparently tied up with the idea that men existed on the other side of the Earth, and Vergilius was therefore suspected of believing in a race of men not descended from Adam. Pope St. Zachary told St. Boniface to convoke a council and to expel Vergilius if he were found to hold to that perverse teaching but, since there is no historical evidence that he ever retracted or was tried, and since he is almost certainly the same who later became Bishop of Salzburg, he must have convinced his censors that he believed in the unity of the human race. His strange cosmology was not the point at issue.

The sphericity of the Earth was upheld by St. Clement, Origen, St. Ambrose, St. Basil, and St. Gregory of Nyssa. Later authors, especially the Venerable Bede (673–735 A.D.), tried to prove it scientifically, Gerbert of Aurillac (Pope Sylvester II, 999–1003 A.D.) recognized it as true, Roger Bacon and St. Albertus Magnus proved it to their satisfaction, and from that time on it became part of the knowledge of nearly all civilized men. But in the early days learned men were on both sides, and Lactantius, and the others who denied it, did so from the mistaken notion that that was the only way in which it was possible for all men to have descended from a common ancestor. Mgr. James F. Loughlin gives the highest praise to the Church for upholding the important doctrine of the universal brotherhood of man before science knew enough to defend the same idea.[2] This is justifiable, but it might have been wiser if the early writers had contented themselves with

[2] *Catholic Encyclopedia* (article on Antipodes), Vol. I, pp. 581–582.

stating the fact and left to advancing knowledge the determining of the form of the Earth and the distribution of man. In saying that, we are, of course, reading our present knowledge into the past, but it is surely wiser for everyone to avoid discussing scientific matters on any but a scientific basis, for knowledge advances and things which may be considered impossible frequently prove to be true.

2. COPERNICUS AND GALILEO

The controversy that developed over Copernican astronomy was the first important one of modern times. It centered particularly around the person of Galileo, and it is the stock case cited as proof that Catholicism is opposed to science. The story has been told repeatedly, but the persistence of misconceptions makes it necessary to outline the discussion and the events that led up to it once more.

We must recall the conditions of the time. The cosmology of Ptolemy, which placed the Earth at the center of the universe, was the basis of the thought of the day and seemed to many to be a necessary foundation for the Christian concept of man's importance in the scheme of the universe. Dante's *Divine Comedy* was built upon it, and it placed Man, the child of God, the ruler of material creation, on the central sphere in the most important place of all. The age was the sixteenth and early seventeenth centuries; people were not yet accustomed to new ideas; the scientific method had been advocated, even practiced by a few, but it had not

32

taken root, and science was still ruled by the authority of Aristotle and Ptolemy.

Yet the seeds of change had been sown. Long before, St. Thomas Aquinas had pointed out that discoveries might well be made which would upset the existing astronomy, and at this particular time there was a tendency abroad in Italy to revive the Platonism of the Fathers with an added tinge of the Pythagorean desire to discover mathematical simplicity in nature. The statement made by Marice de Novara, Professor of mathematics and astronomy at Bologna, that the Ptolemaic system was too complicated to be mathematically harmonious, certainly reflected a growing tendency.

Niclas Koppernigk (1473–1543), a Pole who later changed his name to the Latin form Copernicus, was sent to study in Italy for six years, and there he became a disciple of Novara and came into contact with the old Greek idea that the Earth revolves around the Sun. In fact, he wrote to Pope Paul III that he had learned this from Cicero and Plutarch and had thus begun to think along the lines which led him eventually to formulate his system. After he had fully developed his theory in his own mind, he was prevailed upon by friends to publish an abstract. This was in 1530. Pope Clement VII approved and Copernicus was requested to publish it in full. He delayed, however, until after 1540 and then acquiesced only at the urgent demand of his two friends, Cardinal Schomberg and Bishop Tiedeman Giese of Culm. Because Copernicus was ill at the time, Bishop Giese appointed Rheticus, Copernicus' ablest disciple, to edit the work and, after many difficulties, arranged to have Schröner and Osiander in Nuremburg print it.

Copernicus by this time was nearing his end and was unable to attend even to the proof reading; so that when, on the day he died, the first volume was finally presented to him, he could not see that Osiander had substituted a preface which called the whole work a hypothesis, presented not as a fact but as "an indulgence of the imagination." Osiander did this in good faith in order to turn aside the storm of abuse which he felt would be heaped on the work. He was a Lutheran minister and knew, perhaps better than Copernicus, how the work would be received by Protestants. Copernicus, himself, had dedicated the work to Pope Paul III in order to be protected from the scorn of the mathematicians and philosophers, adding that he made no account of the objections which might be brought by ignorant wiseacres on Scriptural grounds.

This epoch-making work, *The Revolution of the Heavenly Bodies,* presented the view that the Sun is the center of the universe and that the planets, including the Earth, revolve about it. It retained the prevalent notion that the stars are fixed in the outermost sphere of all, but it removed Earth, the abode of man, from its central position. Needless to say, this is incorporated in modern astronomy, but it met much opposition from Protestants on biblical grounds and was rejected by most of the best philosophic and scientific opinion of the day. Some, like Giordano Bruno, espoused the idea and went even further in claiming that the stars themselves were scattered through space at great and varying distances. Bruno's advocacy did the cause no good for he was a heretic to Protestants and Catholics alike and continually attacked all orthodox views. His pantheism and other heresies, not his science, led him finally to the stake.

The Catholic Church, through the Pope and Cardinals, had sponsored Copernicus' work and one need not wonder that there was no opposition from that quarter at first—but this only makes the eventual proceedings against Galileo all the more difficult to understand.

In 1597, Johann Kepler, one of the greatest astronomers of early modern times, ran across an annotated manuscript copy of Copernicus' work belonging to a young astronomer and so discovered that the preface in question was not in the original. He published this fact shortly afterwards and became a strong advocate of the Copernican astronomy. It is a commentary on the state of mind in the Protestant universities of the day that Kepler was driven out of the University of Tübingen and fled to Ingoldstat and Gratz where he continued his studies with the Jesuits. Another notable fact is that, as soon as it was generally understood that Copernicus meant what he had written, Catholic theologians commenced to vie with the Protestants in denouncing the work.

In 1609, Galileo Galilei, professor of mathematics in the University of Padua, hearing that Lippershey, a Dutchman, had invented a new kind of instrument which magnified distant objects, called upon his own knowledge of lenses and constructed his first telescope. In January, 1610, he trained on the sky this instrument with its magnifying power of thirty diameters, and began the series of startling discoveries that gave visual confirmation of Copernicus' system. He saw that Mercury and Venus, the two planets between the Earth and the Sun, had phases like the Moon. Copernicus had claimed that this must be so but he could not observe the fact with his unaided eyes. The five largest of Jupiter's system of satellites revolving around that planet—a solar system in miniature—were next revealed, and then the rough mountainous surface of the Moon and the spots on the Sun moving across its face showed that these orbs did not fit the ancient concept of perfect bodies without blemish.

Galileo, who had long been conversant with Copernicus' work, now became its ardent exponent and proclaimed it not a theory but an established fact. This aroused the ire of the authorities at Rome, and Galileo was summoned before the Congregation of the Index in 1616, where he was detained for some time and forced to promise not to teach Copernican astronomy as a fact. The official documents condemning him declared that the Copernican theory was false and heretical because altogether contrary to Scripture, and the book was suspended until corrected, but it was not until 1620 that Cardinal Gaetani made some trivial changes in it.

Galileo devoted himself to the study of physics for

some years afterwards, and the discoveries which he made would have earned him greater fame than his astronomical researches if it had not been for his conflict with the Church. He was the first serious modern advocate of the experimental method, and he advanced physical science in many lines besides proving error in all sorts of current scientific notions.

In 1624, after Cardinal Barberini, who had been his friend and opposed his condemnation in 1616, had become Pope Urban VIII, Galileo visited Rome again and sought to have the former judgment of the Inquisition annulled. The Pope conferred a pension on him but refused to do as Galileo wished and this so angered him that he commenced work on his famous *Dialogo,* featuring an astronomical discussion between upholders of Ptolemaic and Copernican astronomy—with the Copernicans winning all the disputed points. This, of course, aroused the Congregation of the Index and most of the religious orders again and Galileo found himself in trouble once more. It is true that this second trial, in 1632, was concerned chiefly with the fact that he had broken his pledged word, but he was forced to sign a humiliating retraction. The Benedictine Cardinal Castelli pleaded with the authorities that Galileo had done nothing disrespectful to the Church and stated that nothing could now be done to stop the Earth from turning, but the sentence passed on him once more implied a condemnation of Copernicus.

So, however much we may deplore the lies that have been promulgated concerning this case (Galileo was not imprisoned in a dungeon but detained in the apartment of a friend and, during the actual trial, in that of a member of the Inquisition, and he was denied neither the last sacraments nor Christian burial), we must freely admit that a serious error was made. It was particularly serious for two reasons: first, it allowed Christianity to be tied up with a dying scientific theory as though that theory was a part of religion; and, secondly, it sanctioned an altogether wrong use of Scripture.

Cardinal Bellarmine urged Galileo to be cautious and begged him to wait until absolute proof was forthcoming, saying that it would then be necessary to re-examine the interpretation of the passages in Scripture which his ideas appeared to contradict. Nevertheless, it was a long time before the error was completely corrected. Leave was given in Rome in 1634 to introduce instruments designed to teach Copernican astronomy. Two Catholic priests undertook to defend the Copernican system in 1639 and 1645.[3] An imprimatur was given in Rome for a defence of Copernicus against physical and astronomical objections in 1656. The *Dialogo* was allowed to be included in an edition of Galileo's work in 1744, and Benedict XIV withdrew the universal prohibition in 1757. Yet it was not until 1820 that official permission was granted to publish a textbook containing the Copernican doctrine, and Galileo's works were not re-

[3] Sir Bertram Windle, *The Church and Science,* St. Louis, 1917, pp. 31–32.

moved from the Index until 1822. A new Index, omitting them was published, in 1836.

All this is past history, but the statement that this case negates the Catholic claim of papal infallibility is a live issue, for, if it could be sustained, it would strike at the heart of a dogma of the Church. The reader would do well to consult the Catholic Encyclopedia's article on Infallibility for a full discussion of just what that dogma does imply, but the following points should help to make it clear.

Infallibility, whether of the Church at large, or of the Pope, is affirmed only in regard to matters of faith and morals. Its primary purpose is to maintain, interpret, and assure the legitimate development of Christ's teaching. The Church claims neither impeccability nor inspiration for its members and, in order that a teaching be infallible, the following conditions must be met: (1) The Pope must be speaking in his public official capacity as pastor and doctor of all Christians, that is, as spiritual head of the Universal Church. (2) He must be teaching some doctrine of faith and morals. (3) It must be fully evident that he intends to teach with all the finality of his supreme apostolic authority—that he wishes to determine some point of doctrine in an absolutely final and irrevocable way. He cannot delegate this authority, and hence doctrinal decisions issued by Roman congregations—even when approved by the Pope in the ordinary way—have no claim to infallibility.

Can it be said that the condemnation of Galileo

fulfilled these requirements? That is, did Paul V or Urban VIII so commit themselves to the geocentric doctrine as to impose it upon the Church as an article of faith and did they teach ex-cathedra what is now acknowledged to be untrue? No one questions that they desired to suppress Galileo's teaching, but the important points are these: (1) the decree of 1616 was issued by the Congregation of the Index which is absolutely incompetent to issue a dogmatic decree, and (2) the Pope approved it *in forma communi,* that is, to the extent needed for the purpose intended, namely to prohibit the circulation of writings which were judged harmful.

Evidently, then, it did not meet any of the conditions imposed, and the authors of the decree did not think of it as final and irrevocable. Otherwise Cardinal Bellarmine, a member of the tribunal, would not have suggested shortly afterwards that it might be necessary to re-interpret the pertinent passages in Scripture rather than pronounce as false that which was scientifically demonstrated. In the words of the non-Catholic English astronomer, Richard A. Proctor, "The Catholic doctrine on the subject is perfectly definite; and it is absolutely certain that the decision in regard to Galileo's teaching, shown now to have been unsound, does not in the slightest degree affect the doctrine of infallibility, either of the Pope or of the Church." [4]

---

[4] *Knowledge* (a periodical founded by R. A. Proctor), Vol. IX, p. 274.

CHAPTER III

CONTROVERSIES ABOUT GEOLOGY AND SOME IMAGINARY CONTROVERSIES

1. FOSSILS

FOSSILS are the remains of organisms that have lived in the geologic past and are entombed in the sedimentary rocks over much of the Earth's surface. They may be actual preservations of the hard parts of animals or plants, or merely casts, or molds, or imprints left by some former living thing. In any case, they prove that a certain creature once existed on the Earth and they frequently reveal much about the conditions under which it lived.

The history of man's ideas concerning the significance of these remains is interesting and sometimes amusing. The men of the early Mediterranean civilizations were forced to recognize the existence of fossils since they abound in the rocks of those regions and, as might be expected, some of the early Greeks had correct ideas concerning their significance. Xenophanes, for instance, about 500 B.C., wrote that the shells and fish remains in the rocks of Malta proved that the island had been previously submerged beneath the sea. Aristotle recognized the fact that marine fossils prove that the sea once covered what is now dry land and believed that there had been periodic changes in the relative position of the land and sea. Ovid, Seneca, and Pliny realized that fossils were remains or traces of what had once been living creatures, but they do not appear to have given much thought to the facts or to have developed the logical consequences of this knowledge.[1]

Many of the Greeks, on the other hand, had entirely erroneous notions concerning fossils. These were passed along to the early Middle Ages and many of them have come down practically to modern times. One can find occasional glimpses of the truth, such as the statement of Avicenna the Arab (980–1037 A.D.) that the impressions of aquatic animals in the rocks demonstrated that those rocks were formerly beneath the sea. But, in general, little attention was paid to such things in those days, and this has led many writers to contrast the rigid restrictions which theology imposed upon investigation with the freedom of inquiry that prevailed in pagan times. The idea that motivates this assertion is that Christianity was afraid to admit the existence of fossils because they prove organic and inorganic changes since the time of creation, require great lengths of time in which these changes could occur, and therefore contradict the Mosaic account of creation.

Let us see, however, what these ideas were. Some

[1] For a good brief résumé of early ideas concerning fossils see *The Founders of Geology*, by Sir Archibald Geikie, 1905.

claimed that a plastic force exists in the Earth which forms imitations of shells and bones. This idea is of Greek origin and is taken directly from Aristarchus (374–287 B.C.), a pupil of Aristotle, and it means that fossils are imitations, not remains, of organisms. Those who adhered to this view in the Middle Ages called them *lusus naturae* (freaks of nature) or *lapides figurati* (formed stones).

Another idea was that fossils originated as the result of some occult influence emanating from the stars and were thus organisms in the process of being formed. This notion seems to be traceable to the ideas of Aristotle and other Greeks concerning spontaneous generation, which persisted with few breaks until the time of Pasteur. Aristotle believed that certain organisms, such as the maggots that formed in decaying meat, resulted from the union of a female element present in the meat and a male element somehow emanating from the stars. These stellar emanations were believed capable of controlling all sorts of things on the Earth, and fossils were regarded as one of the results which had somehow failed to materialize fully. Still others perferred to shut their minds entirely to the meaning of fossils and regarded them as creations of the devil permitted by God to tempt men to disbelief.

It is true, particularly after the Reformation, that any idea which made one question the *days* of Genesis and six thousand years, more or less, as the age of the Earth, was questionably orthodox if not absolutely evil. It is also true that if a man is quite certain that the

43

Earth was formed in just so many days, just so many years ago, it will take a great deal to convince him that the idea is fantastic—and this is just what happened. But the important point in this connection is that there were enough Catholic writers who recognized the significance of fossils throughout these times, without being reprimanded by the Church, to prove that the Catholic Church was not concerned over the affair.

Leonardo da Vinci (1452–1519) made an important collection of fossil shells which he studied and classified. He declared positively that they were the remains of once living organisms that had been buried in the silt washed off from the land. Fracastoro (1483–1553), professor of philosophy at the University of Padua and later physician at Verona, was summoned to pass on the nature of the remains found in the stones brought in to repair the Citadel of San Felice at Verona. He stated that they were the remains of animals which lived and multiplied where they were found and, consequently, that they proved the mountains had been successively uplifted above the sea. Cardano (1552) regarded fossil shells as conclusive evidence that the sea once covered the hills in which they were found.

The realization that fossils were actual organic remains spread slowly, but through the sixteenth and into the beginning of the nineteenth century there were many who explained their presence as the result of Noah's deluge which destroyed all living things and left their remains scattered far and wide over the face of the Earth. The difficulty involved in picturing how such things could become a part of the rocks themselves at greatly varying depths and in vertical as well as horizontal strata, was left unexplained. Undoubtedly this easily adopted view retarded investigation and the advance of geological ideas for many years.

This is all the more strange when we consider the clarity with which Nicholaus Stensen had seen the truth in the seventeenth century. His ideas were widely acclaimed at the time and could not be made to imply that all fossils dated from a single, relatively recent period. Stenson (1638–1687) was born in Copenhagen in the Lutheran faith and was trained as an anatomist. He made important discoveries in this field while still a student and was disappointed when, upon the completion of his studies, he was not appointed professor of anatomy. He went to Paris and finally to Italy in 1665, where he settled in Florence and became physician to the Hospital of Santa Maria Nuova. Shortly afterwards he was converted to Catholicism, received the appointment he had sought in his younger days, and returned to Copenhagen. He resigned shortly, however, and returned to Italy to enter Holy Orders. It was after this that he took up the studies in geology which quickly made him as famous in that science as he already was in anatomy. Later he was raised to the Episcopacy and sent to Germany where he completed his life in missionary work, and the geological studies which he had begun were never completed. He did, however, publish the introduction to his contemplated work in 1669, and it is that which earned him the title of the *Father of Modern Geology*. He stated the law which is fundamental to all studies of natural objects, namely, that "if a given body of definite form, produced according to the laws of nature, be carefully examined, it will show in itself the place and the manner of its origin." He applied this to fossils and proved that they were the remains of once living things. He applied it to the formation of sedimentary rocks under the water and showed that the materials in suspension settle with the heaviest at the bottom, that these layers were horizontal when first formed and were deposited on a substratum which was already solid. He observed that such rocks are now tilted, or contorted, or even standing on end and concluded from this that all the the mountains of the earth were not present at the beginning of time but had been formed by the folding and upheaval of sedimentary strata. He also recognized the fact that such a succession of events required great lengths of time.[2]

Any man who sees one thing more clearly than do the others of his generation is worthy of our highest praise, but Stenson saw *many* things that no one had observed before. His name is preserved for students of anatomy by means of the duct which is named after him, and the other accomplishments of this versatile genius are commemorated by the two tablets which

[2] Vide chapter on Stenson in *Twelve Catholic Men of Science* (Sir Bertram Windle, ed.) ; also Sir Archibald Geike, op. cit., Ch. II.

have been placed over his tomb in Florence. The first, erected by the Medici family, commemorates his conversion, his sanctity, and his work for the Church; the second, erected by the geologists of the world met in international congress in Bologna in 1881, commemorates him as "most illustrious both among geologists and anatomists."

There were learned men, however, in Stenson's time as well as later, who did not recognize fossils as organic remains. Martin Lister (1638–1712), a Protestant and an extremely able scientist, published a history of known shells with carefully drawn plates, some of which featured fossil shells for comparison with living species, yet he never believed that the fossils represented actual remains. J. J. Scheuchzer (1672–1733) adopted the view that fossils are relics of the flood and described many of them. His most famous description was that of a fossil skeleton which he believed to have belonged to an antideluvian man. This, *Homo Diluvii Testis*, was published in 1726; and it was nearly one hundred years before Cuvier proved that it was the skeleton of a giant salamander and that it could not date from the time of Noah's flood.

It is only within very recent times that many scholars have held that the flood was restricted to a local occurrence, and that the age of our race on the Earth, as well as the time that has elapsed since creation, are things to be determined, when possible, by scientific investigation. The Catholic Church has never been wedded to any particular chronology in spite of the current notion that the date of Adam's creation has been definitely fixed. The Church has never pronounced on the question at all and the difficulties involved in biblical chronology have been recognized at least since the days of St. Jerome (C. 340–420 A.D.). Consequently it is somewhat absurd to claim that the Church feared the recognition of the true meaning of fossils—the long ages and many changes which they imply.[3] As Father J. A. Zahm wrote, "Biblical chronology, as such, has no bearing on dogma, and for this reason the church has never given the matter any attention, and most likely never will."[4]

If we bear this in mind we will understand that this controversy, like so many others, is based upon the difficulty of forming definite opinions upon natural objects in an age which is not given to observation. Theologians drew their own conclusions, as befitted learned men, but these conclusions were not dictated by the Church and did not represent the Church's opinion. The whole thing proves how slow man is to learn from the natural world around him and how indebted we are for our vaunted modern knowledge to the often blundering and even laborious steps taken by past generations.

[3] Vide *The Bible, Science, and Faith,* by Rev. J. A. Zahm, Baltimore, 1895; also Sir Bertram Windle's *A Century of Scientific Thought and other Essays,* London, 1915.

[4] Zahm, op. cit., p. 300, also pp. 119–175.

2. Noah's Flood

The controversy over the flood is closely linked, as we have seen, with that concerning the significance of fossils. The Fathers, the schoolmen, and the exegetes who followed them, all appear to have believed in the literal interpretation of the biblical account which seems, at first glance, to imply that the flood was universal. Not enough facts were known about nature to cause anyone to question this interpretation and, as fossils gradually came to be recognized as organic remains, and later, when human bones and relics were first found in European caves, their destruction and entombment beneath the waters of a universal flood offered a ready explanation. The science of geology grew very slowly to the point where its well-reasoned conclusions compelled acceptance, but that growth gradually eliminated the possibility of a universal flood and showed that the consequences ascribed to it could not have resulted even if there had been one.

Apparently the Protestant theologian, Isaac Voos, in 1659, was the first to take serious exception to the older views, and Dom Mabillon, O.S.B., gave it as his opinion, upon request of the Congregation of the Index, that the teaching of Voos was against neither faith nor morals. Many geologists took the matter up later and showed that, to intelligent and instructed laymen at least, the Mosaic account did not necessarily imply that the flood covered the whole Earth. Sir Charles Lyell in England, Hugh Miller in Scotland, and Edward

Hitchcock in America were leaders among these. Then, as knowledge of the number and distribution of the types of animals and plants increased, the difficulties involved in accounting for their preservation in the Ark and their immediate redistribution afterwards to far distant continents and islands, grew to insurmountable proportions. There will always be some who will call upon miracles to explain away such difficulties, but this procedure is absolutely contrary to all the principles laid down by Catholic theologians from time immemorial—for it is merely a way of avoiding the facing of facts. This whole problem has always been left open by the Church, and the opinion of the past has been discarded in the light of modern knowledge.

The same is true concerning the universal destruction of man by the flood. There was at first no reason to question the apparent meaning that all men but Noah and his family were destroyed. Once more we must refer the readers to Father Zahm's book, *Bible, Science and Faith,* for a fuller account of this topic, with references.[5] Suffice it to point out here that history, archeology, and ethnology have all made discoveries which render the old interpretation unreasonable. Then, as Father Zahm says, it was seen that the Biblical account accords perfectly well with the view that the flood was confined to a relatively small part of the Earth's surface, and that Moses was concerned with the history of a special people, not with those who had long since migrated into distant lands.

[5] Ibid., pp. 152–174.

It is impossible to admit, with the scientific knowledge now at our command, that all men could have been destroyed by a local deluge at so recent a date. They were far too widely distributed over the face of the Earth. Once again we must point out that though churchmen believed that man had been practically wiped out and that the world had been re-peopled from Noah's stock, this was never more than an opinion held while there was no contrary evidence. Its rejection proves a willingness to learn and to abide by the truth when the truth can be ascertained.

3. SOME IMAGINARY CONTROVERSIES AND FALSE ACCUSATIONS

Before proceeding to the very real controversy over evolution, it will be well to record a few accusations which have been made against the Church, and which are still current, though they have no basis in fact.

It has been written that the Church retarded the development of medicine by refusing to allow the dissection of the human body, and the advocates of this idea cite the decree of Pope Boniface VIII, issued in 1300 A.D., to support their contention, though the decree has nothing whatsoever to do with the case.[6]

The facts are that many of the Crusaders requested that their bodies should be returned home for burial in the event that they died far from home. This was a

---

[6] Vide *The Popes and Science,* by Dr. James J. Walsh, for a complete discussion of this problem and for the full Latin text and translation of the Papal decree.

difficult task for their friends to carry out, since they could not embalm them on the battlefield and transportation was slow and hazardous. The practice of dismembering and cutting up the bodies, boiling the flesh off the bones and carrying them home for burial therefore developed. This is what the Pope forbade and, while some may argue that he had no right to do so, that is entirely beside the point at issue, and no one who reads the decree can still believe that it was directed against the practice of dissection for medical purposes.

This is now generally admitted by all who have looked into the question. As Dr. James J. Walsh points out, even Andrew D. White, in his *History of the Warfare of Science with Theology in Christendom,* admits over and over that such is the case but then writes as though it were not, and claims that the Papal order was misconstrued into a prohibition of dissection for two hundred and fifty years.

The history of anatomy tells a very different story from what White wrings out of it. In 1302 A.D., two years after the publication of the decree, an Italian nobleman died under conditions which suggested poisoning and the judge ordered an autopsy to settle the case. This is the first definite evidence of a dissection but it practically forces the conclusion that dissections were fairly commonplace, and from that time on it is possible, in part at least, to trace the history of dissection in the Italian universities.

Mondino worked in Bologna during the second decade of the fourteenth century and eventually published a textbook on dissection which was used as a guide for two hundred years. He is known to have made a number of dissections and his writings also indicate that he made a great many. Professor Pilcher, in the *Medical Library and Historical Journal* for December, 1906, says that the text of Mondino's book shows that he was "—a man who was habitually dissecting." Within ten years of the decree, there are records of public dissections in Venice at public expense for the benefit of doctors. Long before this, about 1240, a law of the German Emperor Frederick II regulated the practice of medicine and decreed that no surgeon could practice unless he could prove to the medical faculty that he had been teaching and practicing surgery for at least one year and had learned human anatomy in this way. Much later, by 1405, the University of Bologna required that two bodies be furnished for dissection at the medical school each year.

It is now, and always has been, necessary to obtain permission to dissect, and the difficulty of obtaining bodies is reflected in the history of "body snatching"— a method of obtaining them which has always existed. In those days, permission could be obtained most easily and directly from ecclesiastical authorities.

In spite of all this, White quotes a volume in the Benedictine *Literary History of France* as his Catholic authority for the statement that the decree was misconstrued. Dr. Walsh, however, shows that, although this history was begun by the Benedictines, their work was interrupted by the French Revolution and was taken up later on by the Institut de France. The sixteenth volume, the one in question, was written mainly by Pierre Claude François Damon, not by the Benedictines, and is tinged by political and Gallican prejudice. Fifty years before this, someone wrote to Pope Benedict XIV asking whether the decree of Pope Boniface was to be construed as prohibiting dissection, and he received a decidedly negative answer.

These things should be enough to dispose of the myth, but Dr. Walsh quotes from distinguished non-Catholic historians of medicine to show that Italy was the leader in the development of medicine just when, as some would have it, the Popes were suppressing its growth, so we shall reproduce two of these statements here. Puschmann in his *Handbuch der Geschichte der Medizin* wrote: "The successors of Mondino were in a position, owing to the gradual enlightenment of the spirit of the time and the general realization of the importance of anatomy as well as the fostering liberality of the authorities, to make regular, systematic dissections of the human body." [7] This takes us to the end of the fourteenth century. Professor Turner of Edinburgh wrote the article on the History of Anatomy for the first edition of the *Encyclopedia Britannica*. In it he pointed out that "Italy long retained the distinction of giving birth to the first eminent anatomists in Europe, and the glory she acquired in the names of Mondino,

[7] Puschmann, *Handbuch der Geschichte der Medizin,* Vol. I, p. 707.

Achillini, Berengar of Carpi, and Massa was destined to become more conspicuous in the labors of Columbus, Fallopius and Eustachius."

Vesalius (1514–1564) ushered in the golden age of anatomy and his contemporary, Columbus, was one of the greatest of all anatomists. So, in the light of this, the oft-repeated assertion that Vesalius was obliged to perform his dissections in ill-lighted cellars behind barred doors and in constant fear of arrest becomes a little absurd. For Vesalius had gone to Italy from Paris in order to be in the center of the world of medicine. He taught both in Padua and in Bologna, while Columbus was in Rome making autopsies on many ecclesiastics in order to determine what they died of. Dr. Walsh writes: "Columbus, who succeeded Vesalius as lecturer in Padua and was professor at Bologna, was afterwards called to Rome and did many public dissections there. When his great text-book of anatomy was published, it was dedicated to Pope Paul IV. Eustachius, Varolius, Caesalpinus, and Piccolomini, who are the great writers on anatomy, the ardent dissectors of this century after Vesalius and Columbus, were all papal physicians and professors of anatomy at the papal medical school. They had made their reputations by dissection work in other universities, and then were called to the medical school at Rome because they were considered the best candidates for the good work the Popes wanted done there." [8]

[8] *Twelve Catholic Men of Science* (Sir Bertram Windle, ed.), Andreas Vesalius, p. 6. See also Thorndike, *Science and Thought in the Fifteenth Century,* op. cit.

Catholicism and the Progress of Science

The supposed prohibition of analytic and synthetic chemistry is a somewhat similar case, based upon the misconstruction of the decree *Spondent Pariter* of Pope John XXII. This was directed against a certain practice of the alchemists which consisted of mulcting people of their money by pretending to transmute base metals into gold and silver. We have already remarked that alchemy was never in as good repute as astrology, but it was widely practiced and in so far as it was believed true it had a recognized standing. The particular practice which was forbidden by the Pope was a dishonest one which would be recognized as such by civil law today. It had nothing to do with scientific investigation.

A Bull by the same Pope, *Super Illius Specula,* was concerned in the same way with magical practices which were entirely outside of scientific inquiry. And yet that also has been absurdly construed as a Papal prohibition of science.

CHAPTER IV

ORGANIC EVOLUTION

1. THE PROBLEM

THE variety and the wide distribution of living creatures on this earth are among the most striking facts of nature which confront man and demand explanation. At least since the time of Aristotle men have been engaged in studying and classifying the known varieties and in speculating concerning the connections and distinctions between them, though it is only in comparatively recent times, since all the continents have been explored, that a real appreciation of the truly amazing diversity of types has been possible. The similarity between many natural groups of animals or plants, coupled with the many varieties that have been developed from single stocks by breeding domesticated types, have always inclined thoughtful naturalists to the view that there may exist a genetic connection between all living things, or, at the very least, between those which are similar in structure and habits.

There are only two possible explanations of this great variety of organisms. Either each type came into existence full-formed at a particular time and in a particular place by a separate act of creative force; or, all have developed or evolved out of one or a number of original forms. The first explanation is the doctrine of *special creation* and it claims, more specifically, that each species of animal and plant has been created as it now is and that variation has been confined to certain alterations within the individual species—the species itself being fixed and immutable. The second explanation is the doctrine of organic evolution which claims that life commenced in the form of simple, unspecialized cells and that life has developed from life, with change and specialization, until the present types came into existence. It recognizes that development has ceased in certain organisms but claims that it is still in operation in many others and, while it does not *necessarily* refer all living things to one original, ancestral cell, the consensus of opinion among naturalists favors this idea. From this point of view evolution is simply *the process* which has operated on the Earth's surface to bring the life about us to its present state of development. It has nothing whatsoever to say about the origin of life, and it does not remove the logical necessity for a first cause. Why is it, then, that when evolution was first introduced in its modern form by Darwin in 1859, after some years of nearly total eclipse, it met with such resistance and brought so much abuse on the head of Darwin? Why was it regarded by so many as dealing the final death blow to Christianity?

The answer to this question must be long and involved, for it is a difficult question at best. First, we must realize that special creation had somehow come to be regarded by many as a Christian dogma instead of as what it really was, a relatively recent idea based upon the notion of the fixity of arbitrarily defined *species*. Second, many of the early proponents of evolution went out of their way to attach to it a purely materialistic interpretation. That is, they claimed that it could be explained as the operation of pure chance and therefore did away with the necessity of a First Cause. This attempt to tie up a process of nature with a philosophic theory has done much to cause religiously minded people to look with horror on evolution, and it is the fault of such men as Haeckel and his followers.

In the third place, many theologians totally missed the intrinsic beauty of the idea of evolution and the chance which it offered to cease thinking of God as perpetually compelled to tinker with His creation, and to regard Him instead as capable of making things make themselves. These men attacked evolution on scientific grounds, about which they knew nothing, and failed to confine their objections to the false theological and philosophical conclusions which were drawn from the theory.

Evolution met as much opposition from scientists as from any other men, but with this difference: as soon as the weight of the evidence which Darwin had gathered together was appreciated, the majority of scientists changed their views and came over to his side. There were scientists who never did capitulate, just as there were theologians who were wise enough to see at once that Theism—the belief in a personal, all-powerful Creator—was perfectly compatible with

59

evolution. There were many people, and there are some left today, who never took the trouble to find out that evolution, a process which is believed to have operated, and Darwinism, which is Charles Darwin's particular explanation of how the process operated, are not at all one and the same thing.

The whole controversy shows the tendency, on the one hand, to cling to cherished notions regardless of their lack of foundation on fact, and on the other hand, to proclaim that at last Christianity is dead. We do not owe it to either of these factions that organic evolution is now regarded by many as established in science and in no way opposed to Christianity. We owe that to the patient students on both sides who were superior to the hysteria of the moment and who, throughout it all, sought the truth.

The question whether or not evolution is true is a scientific question which can only be answered by scientific evidence. We have no revelation to guide us and no intuitions which can settle the matter. But questions concerning the theological and philosophical implications of the idea can only be settled by those versed in such matters—a fact which scientists are too apt to overlook. The investigation of the evidences for evolution must also settle the case for special creation, for that, by its very nature, cannot be investigated directly; it is an assumption which is only justified if the evolutionary alternative cannot be upheld. For this reason we shall present in the next chapter an outline of the evidences for organic evolution and point out how difficult it is to explain many aspects of our knowledge on any other basis. But before doing this, we shall review the history of the concept itself, in order to gain a better appreciation of certain of the problems involved.

2. History of the Evolutionary Concept before Darwin

Many writers [1] have granted to Empedocles (495–435 B.C.) the right to be considered the originator of the concept of evolution, but most agree with H. F. Osborne that "with Aristotle we enter a new world. He towered above his predecessors, and by the force of his genius created Natural History." According to Father Zahm "He, then, and not Empedocles, should be regarded as the father of the evolution theory." [2] For Aristotle based his views of nature on observation and experiment. He did not give up all the teachings of Plato, his instructor, but he did discard the idea that *a priori* reasoning led to truth concerning natural things, and that is why most discussions of early science begin with him. Many of his beliefs are absurd in the light of modern knowledge, but we must remember the meager factual background which he possessed and the paucity of methods of investigation at his command. It will indeed be surprising if more than a few of our modern scientific views have even an historical importance after the lapse of a similar number of cen-

[1] Vide especially Henry Fairfield Osborne, *From Greeks to Darwin,* 1908; also H. H. Newman, *Readings in Evolution, Genetics, and Eugenics,* rev. ed., 1925.

[2] Rev. J. A. Zahm, *Evolution and Dogma,* Chicago, 1896, p. 28.

turies. On the other hand, in the *History of Animals,* Aristotle wrote: "We must not accept a general principle from logic only, but must prove its application to each fact. For it is in fact that we must seek general principles, and these must always accord with facts." He also perceived the importance of heredity and of reversion to type and had a clear idea of the whole scheme of successive life forms from plants, through animals, to man, and was a believer in intelligent design in nature.

Little investigation into the problem of evolution was carried on from Aristotle's day up to the time of Buffon and Lamarck in the eighteenth century. The Romans accepted the Greek views about scientific matters without much alteration, and the early Fathers of the Church considered the theological applications of all the scientific theories and philosophical systems which were extant at the time, particularly their relation to Genesis. They added no new observations but it is extraordinary how far-sighted some of them were and how perfectly they laid the philosophical and theological foundations for what man was to discover through scientific studies so many hundreds of years later. These men, in the great centers of learning, were confronted by educated men and systems of thought coming from all over the civilized world and were forced to justify their faith and show that it was not contrary to human knowledge.

Origen, at Alexandria (late second and early third century), was one of the first to meet the objections of the pagan and other philosophers. He was one of the greatest representatives of the Alexandrian School and established there a school of his own to train others in exegetical methods, but it is important to recall that he taught his students contemporary science before taking up the study of Scripture. Origen's teaching, which interests us most in the present connection, is that the universe and all that it contains were created *simultaneously*. This was an opinion which he advanced in order to circumvent the view that the days of Genesis were twenty-four hour periods—for that was what he could not admit. This view led him to a purely allegorical interpretation of Genesis and much of the rest of the Scriptures, and obviated, of course, any possibility of a concept of evolution, since it allowed no change from the beginning. He regarded human souls as spirits imprisoned in the flesh because of transgressions against God, so there was no need even for their creation, as new human bodies came into existence. Naturally, such complete allegorism brought about a reaction which was most marked among· the great teachers of the Syrian school. St. Ephrem rejected the notion of the simultaneity of creation and taught that God created the substance of heaven and earth in the beginning out of nothing but that He formed all else out of this substance subsequently in six actual days of twenty-four hours each. St. Basil, in his sermons, rejected all allegorism and preached the literal interpretation of Genesis.

St. Gregory of Nyssa (approx. 332–398), St. Basil's

brother, appears to be the first who clearly conceived the idea that God created matter in a formless state and gave it the power to develop.[3] He denied special intervention by God at any time and attributed development, or evolution, to secondary causes instituted by God at the instant of creation. St. Augustine developed the concept still more clearly. He taught that God created primordial matter by an act of will, out of nothing, but created all else by the operation of secondary causes, or what we now call natural laws, instituted by Him. This is the theory of *absolute natural evolution* which allowed for no interference even in the production of living from non-living matter or in the formation of man's body.

This Christian naturalism in its extreme development was only possible while spontaneous generation was considered a fact established by observation. It had its roots in the desire to avoid the errors of the pagan philosophers who ascribed so many movements and developments in nature to the manipulations of a host of deities, and to ascribe everything instead to one, all-powerful God. It was philosophically satisfying and completely in accord with the science of the day, and it held the field until well along in the Middle Ages.

In the present state of our scientific knowledge, with spontaneous generation ruled out, it is difficult to sub-

[3] Dorlodot, op. cit., pp. 67–68, shows that St. Gregory of Nyssa claimed that St. Basil's true meaning was misunderstood because he necessarily used language which appealed to the multitude, and that he, St. Gregory, taught nothing in his own system which was contrary to St. Basil's philosophic and scientific views.

scribe to this theory. Many believe that life *must* have come from inorganic matter by natural means at some time in the past, when conditions were just right, but this is only a speculation which is not yet attested by science.[4]

The evolutionary view of the Fathers, just outlined, was a broad cosmologic view of development which cannot be compared in detail to our modern concept of organic evolution because it had to be capable of accommodating repeated additions to the sum of living things by means other than the development of life from life, but it shows that the idea of evolution of matter, once created, is in perfect harmony with Catholic doctrine.

St. Thomas Aquinas limited this view of evolution somewhat by what he believed to be scientific evidence but remained faithful to the spirit of Christian Naturalism—that is, he continued to explain natural phenomena, so far as his scientific knowledge would permit him, by means of secondary causes and not by direct intervention.[5] Aristotle thought he had established that the species which originated by spontaneous

---

[4] Many experiments are being performed along these lines. Experiments with colloids appear to indicate where the solution of the problem may lie, but if experiment ever succeeds in showing how life can come from non-living matter under ordinary natural conditions, the problem of spontaneous generation will be re-opened, and all sorts of difficulties will arise in connection with evolution, unless it can also be proved that those conditions existed only once and have not been repeated.

[5] Vide Dorlodot, op. cit., pp. 87–94, and appendix IV, for a complete discussion of this point, with references.

generation could not reproduce themselves. He believed they were developed out of putrefying matter fecundated by emanations from the Sun and the stars and that they had to be repeatedly so produced. St. Thomas accepted this as a fact and was driven by it to declare that the first individuals of the higher species were not generated out of the Earth by the power of the stars, since they did reproduce themselves, but were directly created by God. So it was after the writings of Aristotle were re-introduced into Europe by the Arabs, at a time when no one thought of experimenting and testing his statements, that his erroneous ideas caused the theory of absolute natural evolution to be modified to make room for the special creation of many types of life.

Father Zahm shows that the scholastic doctrine of species is not, as often claimed, incompatible with evolution.[6] The scholastics regarded metaphysical and logical species as immutable just as the laws of thought and logic are unchangeable, but they made no such claim in the case of physiological species. Their knowledge of the latter was necessarily vague and they did not attempt to decide, without any evidence, whether species of animals and plants could be included in the category of immutable metaphysical species or not.

The true significance of the natural groupings to which the term, species, has been applied still eludes us, but the idea of fixity of species, which was current before evolution superseded it, is of relatively recent

[6] *Evolution and Dogma,* op. cit., pp. 313–319.

origin. It was not handed down from antiquity or, as some still believe, as a legacy from literalists in biblical interpretation. It dates from John Ray (1627–1705) who defined species as "a group with many character-istics in common and freely interbreeding." Linnaeus (1707–1778), one of the great naturalists of the eight-eenth century, developed modern biological nomencla-ture and helped to fix the idea of species as specially created entities which could not develop from or into any other species. He admitted variation and develop-ment within species by hybridization but considered species themselves immutable.

Linnaeus' influence therefore retarded the develop-ment of the evolutionary concept for the time being, but it turned men's minds towards the detailed study and classification of animals and plants and prepared the factual basis for further speculation.

All this time spontaneous generation was still con-sidered possible and this effectively prevented any serious study of evolution since it left the way open for repeated additions to the sum total of living things from inorganic sources. Francesco Redi (approx. 1626–1697), of Florence was the first to give experi-mental proof that spontaneous generation did not occur by placing meat in a jar, covering it with fine gauze, and showing that no maggots developed when flies were excluded. His claim brought out all sorts of ob-jections but he triumphed over his opponents tem-porarily—until the microscope was brought to bear on the problem. This showed the existence of countless animalcules which were not revealed to the naked eye but were capable of penetrating the gauze—and thus the whole problem was reopened.

The next to dispute it was Father Spallanzani (1729–1799), a distinguished scientist, but even his demonstration that, provided the necessary precautions were taken, no animalcules would develop in decaying flesh, was not sufficient to destroy the idea, and it remained for Pasteur (1822–1895) to give it the coup de grâce from which it has not yet recovered.

The next important name that we encounter in a survey of evolution is that of Buffon (1707–1788), a contemporary of Linnaeus who, however, thought along quite different lines. He did not believe that man-made classifications represent distinct entities in nature but he was, on the contrary, looking for connections between types. He recognized the modifying effect of environment on organisms, the struggle for existence between individuals and species, and believed that these modifications could be inherited. He was, therefore, an evolutionist with a theory of how evolution came about.

Erasmus Darwin (1731–1802), grandfather of Charles Darwin, was another of the same generation who helped to advance our knowledge of evolution. He believed that new characteristics develop, in response to a need, as the result of the individual's exertions. They are, thus, internal in origin and represent an actual advance which can be transmitted to successive generations. Also, he expressed clearly the idea of the length of time required for the development of all creatures on the Earth by a slow process of transformation.

Jean Baptiste Lamarck (1744–1829) is generally considered the founder of the modern theory of evolution and yet, as we shall see, the theory was not in favor until many years had elapsed after his death. We shall consider his ideas together with those of Darwin and other writers in greater detail later. For the present, we must be content to point out that Lamarck reached his conclusions after long study of animals and plants, and that he added more data to the factual evidence for evolution than anyone else had done since the time of Aristotle.

Georges Cuvier (1769–1832) was an ardent advocate of the fixity of species besides being the real founder of the science of paleontology. It was he who finally settled the controversy over the significance of fossils and established the value of the fossil record in the study of Earth history, but he ridiculed Lamarck's evolutionary ideas and entered into a bitter controversy with Geoffrey St. Hilaire (1772–1844) who defended evolution, particularly Buffon's concept of the direct action of the environment in producing modification. In this way Cuvier's great prestige retarded the development of evolution for at least another generation.

3. Lyell and Darwin

Thus the seed of the evolutionary concept, sown so many generations before, germinated and withered again before it finally came to fruit. Something else was needed before it could be generally accepted and it was largely the genius of Sir Charles Lyell, the English geologist, that prepared the way for its ultimate triumph. At the beginning of his life's work, geology was still wedded to the theory of catastrophism—the belief that the surface of the Earth had undergone successive destructions during which volcanism, mountain building, upheavals of the continents, and great climatic changes overwhelmed every living thing, leaving the lands desolate and ready to be re-peopled by a new creation. While this view prevailed there was no chance to think of evolution. Sir Charles Lyell's wide acquaintance with geological literature, coupled with his original studies, led him to re-introduce the fundamental geological law that *the present is the key to the past,* which had been stated by Buffon and insisted on by the Scotch geologist Hutton. According to this, the processes which caused all the past changes on the surface of the Earth, erosion by rivers, waves, wind, and ice, uplift and folding of mountains, volcanism, etc., are the self-same, slow processes that are actively shaping the Earth today. Geology, from that day, became the study of inorganic evolution and the theory of *uniformitarianism* replaced the older one. Modern geology recognizes changes in the rate of certain of these processes from time to time but the uniformitarian idea is fundamental to all the important developments which geology has undergone and it makes the view of continuous organic evolution possible.

Charles Darwin (1809–1882) was greatly influenced by Lyell's work. He had travelled extensively as a naturalist and, at the beginning of his protracted illness, he settled down to study and to think over the materials which he had collected. Early during this period he read Malthus' *On Population* which emphasizes so vividly the effect on the human race of the struggle for existence resulting from the more rapid increase of individuals than of the food supply, and this appears to have been the last thing necessary to set his mind to work on the theory of Natural Selection as an explanation of the evolutionary changes which, he was already convinced, had occurred. Darwin labored on for twenty years, accumulating evidence by experiment and observation and reading everything that bore upon the topic, before he could be induced to present his work to the world. This is what distinguishes him most sharply from all those who preceded him and, no matter what the final verdict on his theory of Natural Selection may be, it is to him that the acceptance of evolution as a process is due. The seed of evolutionary idea had long been present in people's minds but it did not develop until Darwin suggested a factor that might explain how it could come about.

Lyell had been urging Darwin to publish for years, but it was a strange chance which finally forced his hand. For Alfred Russel Wallace sent him his own brief paper, written half way around the world from where Darwin worked, outlining the theory of Natural Selection almost as Darwin had done it. This was published on July 1, 1858, along with a letter from Darwin to the American botanist Asa Grey, dated 1857, and outlining his views, as well as an abstract of Darwin's work written many years before. But, in spite of this, it was not until the appearance of Darwin's *Origin of Species by Means of Natural Selection, or the Preservation of Favored Races in the Struggle for Life* that the mass of evidence which he presented began to compel assent, and evolution took its place as one of the dominant concepts which direct men's thoughts.

In the next chapter we shall outline the general types of evidence upon which evolution is based and then survey the newer trends in evolutionary science since Darwin's day.

CHAPTER V

EVIDENCES OF EVOLUTION AND RECENT TRENDS IN BIOLOGICAL SCIENCE

1. EVIDENCES OF EVOLUTION

From Domestication

Many domesticated species have been so profoundly modified that the original wild type can no longer be identified. Furthermore, the various breeds of dogs, horses, and so forth, as well as domesticated plants, differ among themselves far more than do many wild species, and any naturalist, coming across them under natural conditions, would unhesitatingly class them as separate species. All this has been accomplished by man by means of artificial selection of natural variations in a comparatively short time and it throws serious doubt upon the validity of our idea of species besides rendering the concept of fixity of species very improbable. William B. Scott calls attention to the following case of rapid alteration of a species under conditions of isolation as described by Darwin.[1] The Portuguese navigator Zarco set free a doe and her newly born litter of rabbits on the small island of Porto Santo, not far

[1] William B. Scott, *The Theory of Evolution*, N. Y., 1919, pp. 37–39.

from Madeira, about the year 1420. She was from one of the domestic races derived from the wild European rabbit and, in the absence of any other land mammals, her litter grew and multiplied rapidly. After four and a half centuries of such isolation the Porto Santo rabbit had become so different from any known rabbits that Haeckel described it as a new species. Specimens were taken to Europe. They were smaller than the native rabbits, differently colored and marked, extraordinarily wild, active, and nocturnal in their habits, and they would not associate or breed with the many types of rabbits which were put with them in succession. According to all accepted standards a new species had formed in a remarkably short time.

From Comparative Anatomy

The study and comparison of all forms of animal life shows that there are a number of distinct types of structures each of which is characteristic of a great group of animals. For instance, the flipper of a whale, the wing of a bat, the leg of a horse, the hand and arm of a man are all built on exactly the same fundamental plan, modified of course for swimming, flying, running, and the various uses to which man's arm can be applied. Some bones, nerves, and muscles are enlarged, others atrophied, or bones are fused together, but they can be definitely referred to one type whose owners belong to the *class* of mammals. The wing of a bird shows similarity of structure to that of a bat and of a pterodactyl or flying reptile (now extinct). The ways in which the parts are arranged in order to accomplish the purpose for which all are constructed differ rather markedly, but the fundamental structures are the same and these three types are classed under one *order*—vertebrates. On the other hand, crustacea (crabs and lobsters and certain other types together with their ancestral forms) have a certain definite plan which is different from that of the vertebrates. The various types of shell fish have another, sponges still another, and so forth. Then there are certain organs in individuals which appear to serve no useful purpose but which can be readily explained on the theory that they were useful to the individuals from which these have evolved. Man has a large number of these, such as the functionless muscles which raise the hair, move the ears, or wag the tail—the skeletal remnant of which still remains at the base of the spine. These are the *vestigial structures* which are understandable from the point of view of evolution but from no other.

The structural evidence first cited does not show any connection between the main groups or indicate how one can be derived from the other. It shows a common plan within the groups and suggests a plan common to all living things. The study of vestigial organs confirms this but leaves the discovery of the connection between the major types of living things to paleontology. The recognition of evolution leads one further; it does not deny the plan but it indicates in general how the Planner worked.

75

From Embryology and Blood Tests

These evidences are linked together here because they also indicate a common plan and do not *prove* a genetic relationship, but they increase its likelihood to a marked degree. The fact is that the development of the embryos of all vertebrates, and other orders, show the same plan more unmistakably than do the adults, and many connections between dissimilar organisms have been traced through the study of embryos.

Blood testing proves nothing definite except chemical similarity or dissimilarity of the blood serum of the organisms tested, but it discloses the fact that organisms which had been placed close together by comparative anatomy or embryology also have chemically similar blood so that their development from some common ancestor becomes even more likely. The horse and the zebra, for instance, have very similar blood; even the horse and a distantly related mammal such as the whale show some similarity, birds and reptiles also show some, but mammals and reptiles or mammals and birds show none at all.

From Paleontology

If evolution is true there should be a record of many of the forms entombed in the rocks as fossils. The record will be incomplete because fossils need very special conditions in order to form at all and many, once formed, have been destroyed by alteration of the inclosing rock and by erosion.[2] But, incomplete as it is, the record is there and it gives the most important evidence for evolution. The oldest fossil remains are those of simple, soft-bodied creatures and successive geological ages are marked by more and more complex forms of life. Vertebrates did not appear until long after all the main groups of invertebrates were in existence. The first of these were fish, some of which later developed auxiliary lungs, and after this amphibians came into existence. These start their life breathing the air in water by means of gills and are subsequently transformed into air breathers as, for example, present-day frogs and toads. Amphibians may be completely adapted to life on land after their metamorphosis but they must return to water to breed. They were followed by the reptiles who were equipped with lungs from birth and fitted for life on land, so much so that even those which took to the sea again breathed air. The first birds were reptilian in many respects but they slowly lost most of their ancestral characters and developed into modern types. Early in the history of the reptiles certain groups exhibited a number of mammalian characteristics—then the mammals appeared. The first were small creatures, the most primitive were egg-layers, then marsupials such as the kangaroo, and finally placentals to which group the majority of living animals belong.

[2] Vide any good textbook of historical geology, e.g., *Outlines of Historical Geology*, by Schuchert and Dunbar, 3rd ed., 1937, for a discussion of the conditions necessary for the formation and the preservation of fossils.

There are gaps in the evidence, to be sure, but the sequence of types is established with surprising completeness, and the evolution of countless groups can be traced in detail from their inception through many specializations, even to extinction; while many others develop little and remain much the same through immense lengths of time. Truly, the story that paleontology recounts is epitomized in the definition of evolution—from simple beginnings, life has developed from life with change and specialization until the many varieties now in existence came into being.

From Distribution

If evolution is true each animal and plant has come from pre-existing ones and each type from a pre-existing type. Therefore each group of related animals or plants must have had a common ancestral form and a definite place of origin. A species arises, spreads, becomes modified as it goes and new species develop but show their common origin in their structures and blood. If the component parts of the related group are widespread the ancestral form must be sought at the center of dispersal and the paleontologic record should reveal some of the missing connections.[3] An examination of a few cases will show that this is exactly what is found to be true. For example, the camel in Asia and the llama in South America are closely related according to all criteria, and the paleontologic record reveals

[3] For a concise statement of the evidence see particularly W. B. Scott, *The Theory of Evolution,* op. cit.

78

that the camel arose and developed in North America before the migrations to its present abodes took place and the existing distinctions became so marked. The ancestral form subsequently died out. Similarly, the tapirs which are now confined to the Orient and South America once ranged over the whole of the northern hemisphere. They became extinct in the centers from which distribution occurred so that the existing varieties have no evident connection.

Following an analogous line of reasoning, it was determined that the paleontologic record of the Ceratopsians or horned dinosaurs in both Europe and North America indicated a common origin somewhere in Central Asia, and the expedition sent out to search the region of the Gobi discovered the ancestral form Protoceratops.

During the geological period known as the Tertiary, which occurred just before the last ice age and the beginning of modern time—the period during which the mammals developed—North and South America were first connected, then disconnected for a long time and finally connected again as they are today by the Isthmus of Panama. At first the mammalian inhabitants of both continents were much alike and intermingled freely but, during the long time when the continents were separated by a body of water, they developed very differently and these dissimilar types intermingled when the connection was re-established. The point is that during isolation under different environments, different types arose out of the original stocks. The same is noted on continental islands, that is, on those which lie near and are structurally a part of the mainland. They possess a fauna which was similar to that of the mainland at the time of their last connection and, if they have been separated for long, they will exhibit types which are quite different from those on the nearest continent. England, for instance, was comparatively recently disconnected from Europe and its fauna is practically identical with that of the continent. Madagascar, on the other hand, has been separated from Africa for a comparatively long time so that many changes have occurred. The continent of Australia illustrates this very well since marsupials and monotremes (egg-laying mammals) were the highest forms of life when it became a separate land. Placental mammals which developed on the larger continents never reached Australia and the marsupials developed many forms not known in regions where they were superseded by placentals. It is true that, when white man first went to Australia, mice were present but these were either carried on driftwood or were taken in the boats by means of which the aborigines migrated to that continent.

According to the theory of evolution the absence of an organism from any particular place does not necessarily mean that the environment is not proper for it— it means that it developed elsewhere and never had a chance to migrate to the place in question. Gypsy and brown-tailed moths and the Japanese beetles in America, rabbits in Australia, mongeese in Jamaica, cacti and century plants in the Mediterranean lands and South Africa, horses and oxen in North America, and the Porto Santo rabbit are all examples of organisms that thrive in an environment from which they were excluded by impassable natural barriers until man transported them. For the same reason tropical South America, Africa, and Australia which have very similar climates, possess radically different flora and fauna, and oceanic islands far removed from the mainland always have a peculiarly limited fauna.

This distribution of animals and plants so briefly outlined is puzzling, meaningless in fact, unless it is viewed from the evolutionary standpoint. When this is done the findings of paleontology, the scheme of relationships derived from the study of comparative anatomy, and the peculiarities of distribution, have an evident meaning; and the complex relationships of organisms fit into a definite pattern in spite of the imperfection of our knowledge.

The idea of special creation can, of course, be made to explain everything but without reason or order. Why, for instance, should islands which are rarely visited by birds from the continental mainlands, such as the Hawaiian group, exhibit a bird fauna peculiar to themselves while those near the mainland have a bird population so similar to that of the neighboring continent? If species are fixed, inaccessibility should have nothing to do with it. This, together with many of the other facts mentioned, does not prove evolution, but, by using the evolutionary hypothesis in their explanation the facts become intelligible.

It is exactly because evolution brings order into and gives meaning to so many and such varied studies that it is now generally accepted as true.

2. THEORIES OF THE MANNER OF EVOLUTION

In the preceding chapter we traced the history of the evolutionary concept up to the time of Lamarck and Darwin. Now we must pick it up at that point and deal briefly with its more recent aspects.

Lamarck believed that evolution could be explained by means of the gradual development of new organs as the direct result of the needs of the organism, and that this development is in direct ratio to the employment of the organ. In other words, an organ comes into existence because the organism must have it in its environment, and as long as it is used it is strengthened and developed, but as soon as it ceases to be useful it is atrophied and disappears. This is the *theory of use and disuse* which was necessarily supplemented by the *inheritance of acquired characteristics;* that is, any mark or change impressed upon an individual during its lifetime can be passed on to the next generation. The second theory has given rise to more discussion, perhaps, than any other single suggested factor in evolution and, in spite of a vast amount of experimental work, it is not yet certain whether it works or not.

Charles Darwin emphasized different factors. His

evolutionary theory depends upon four things: (1) prodigality of production; (2) heredity; (3) variation; and (4) natural selection. The first emphasizes the vast quantity of living things that are born into the world destined to be destroyed before they reach biological maturity, that is, before they are capable of reproducing their kind. This factor is of fundamental importance since it furnishes the raw material on which the others can work. Heredity guides the course of life by determining that the young should always be of the same general type as the parent. Variation refers to the small variations between individual descendants of the same parents; variations in size, color, markings, and so forth. Natural selection means that, in the long run, nature will *select* the advantageous variations—those which best fit their possessor to its environment—by the simple process of killing off the individuals with less favorable variations. This results in what Herbert Spencer called the *Survival of the Fittest* and, in order that this may work, the variations must be continuous, must all be equally transmissible, and must include all possible changes from the parent stock—that is, they must not tend toward a particular type.

Darwin also emphasized the importance of the use and disuse of organs and developed a special theory, long since discarded, to show how changes caused in an organ by this means could also change the germ plasm, that is, the reproductive cells, and be inheritable.

In 1896 Bateson challenged the idea of continuous variations and suggested that discontinuous variation might be at the bottom of the discontinuity of species. Somewhat later August Weissman denied that characteristics acquired during the lifetime of the parents could be inherited by the offspring and developed the theory which supposes that the germ plasm is set aside in each individual during the early stages of its embryonic development and cannot be altered by anything that happens to the individual later in life. This theory probably carries the distinction between body cells and germ cells, as well as the isolation of the germ cells, too far, but it has been fruitful in many ways. Also, it left natural selection alone in the field as a possible explanation of evolution and thus served to show up its weaknesses.

The Dutch botanist DeVries, along with a number of others, undertook the study of mutations and, in 1904, advanced the hypothesis that these, not chance variations, were the basis of evolutionary changes. Mutations are sudden changes that appear in an individual and represent actual changes in the germ plasm. Many of them are no greater than the chance variations which Darwin stressed, but they are passed on by heredity while the others seem to die out with the individual. Darwin had investigated mutations in the course of his work but had concluded that they did not occur with sufficient frequency to be important. The evidence which DeVries and his co-workers accumulated represented, therefore, a real step forward and, in the course of their researches, they turned up the writings of Gregor Mendel which had been buried in an obscure scientific periodical but which were destined to change the trend of evolutionary research.

Mendel (1821–1884), a monk in the Augustinian monastery in Brün, Austria, experimented on the hybridization of plants and kept a record of the results with mathematical precision. He worked with single characters such, for example, as the color of the seeds of sweet peas. He crossed yellow-seeded with green-seeded peas and noted that the first hybrid generation bore only yellow seeds. He allowed these to cross-fertilize and found that the next generation bore yellow and green seeds in the ratio of three yellow to one green and that in subsequent generations all of the green and one-third of the yellow bred true, but that the remaining two-thirds of the yellow produced two-thirds yellow, one-third green, and so forth through succeeding generations. Mendel named the factor which impressed itself on the first generation *dominant* and the one which was temporarily submerged *recessive,* and time has proved the extreme value of these concepts; but the real importance of his work was the discovery that factors which will blend for one generation will subsequently segregate out as pure strains and breed true according to a determinable law. Thus new unit characters which may arise as mutations can be transmitted by heredity.

The widespread experimental study of heredity which has followed these discoveries has exposed the material basis of heredity both in animals and plants. New plant species have been developed in the laboratory—types, that is, which breed true and which are sterile towards the parent stock. In consequence of these things, we now recognize once more that our term *species* refers to something with a real existence. We do not regard species as forever fixed and immutable. Neither do we think of them any more as representing merely the present, transitory condition of something in a continual flux.

The incorporation of the Mendelian laws into the scheme of evolution places less emphasis on the struggle for existence and more on the appearance of new characters which become incorporated in the species. These inheritable variations or mutations appear (we do not yet know how); they are incorporated in the existing species according to the laws of heredity; natural selection helps weed out unfit types; geographic isolation prevents new hybridization and hastens the development of new species.

Mutations do not appear to be determined by environment, though they are possibly guided by it, and may be a response to profound changes which include a transformation in the inner world of bodily organs and fluids, as well as external change. They may be initiated by the natural bombardment of germ cells by cosmic rays or by emanations from radio-active substances in a manner comparable to the results obtained by experimental bombardment of seeds by "fast neutrons" or by X-rays which now gives promise of causing true mutations in plants. These, and many now unknown factors, may be parts of the explanation of change or mutation, but, even if they are, they do not explain the course of evolution. Natural selection, incapable of initiating change, can only explain why certain things do not exist, for it really means the struggle of an already developed individual or type to adjust itself to conditions and survive. So, admitting, as the evidence compels us to, that life has advanced from simple to complex throughout long periods of time, it seems as though there must be a guiding principle which has directed the development along some planned line. If the environmental changes revealed by geology had advanced steadily in a definite direction, it might be possible to find in that the cause of a progressive change in life from simple to complex in the particular direction along which life has evolved; but geologic changes have not been of that kind. There has been no progressive change in the character of the atmosphere, the land masses have not become steadily larger or smaller, higher or lower; climate has not changed slowly but continually from wet to dry, cold to warm, or vice versa. Instead, changes of all kinds have been cyclic—mountains were raised and torn down, seas encroached upon the land and withdrew again, climates became arid and then moist again, so that, if these changes were the guides of evolution, the process should end exactly where it began.

In any case it would be difficult to explain why life should originate out of inorganic matter for purely natural reasons, for living things have nothing like the survival value of inorganic matter and the higher forms of life have less than the lower; that is, they are more markedly different from their surroundings and must struggle harder to exist. Also, many organisms have developed specializations which finally assured their destruction as though some inner, driving force compelled them to continue a certain development once it had begun. These are some of the reasons why most paleontologists have felt the need for some positive factor in evolution to explain the upward surge of life which their study reveals.

Theories of directed evolution or orthogenesis have long existed and explain this upward surge either as resulting from a mystic force not susceptible of scientific investigation (which is merely a defeatist way out of the dilemma), or because definite, determined lines of evolution along which life progressed were laid down by a Lawgiver. This is so completely in keeping with Catholic doctrine that God works by secondary causes, and so in line with the rest of science and its ideas of causality and natural law that it appears to be the most fruitful concept of all. But whatever the cause, directed evolution is generally believed to be one of the fundamental laws of organic evolution.[4]

3. EVOLUTION AND THE CATHOLIC

The Christian reader must bear in mind that directed evolution means God working through secondary causes which He instituted; and if it seems to point more directly to God than does evolution working by

[4] Vide H. H. Newman, op. cit., especially pp. 27–45.

some apparently pure-chance method, such as natural selection, this is merely an illusion. It does not relieve us from the necessity of finding out how the Creator directs it, and if we understand fully that evolution is only a process in any case, and that a First Cause is clearly indicated by all our knowledge, we have no right to assume, before the evidence is complete, that one way or another must be *the* way in which God has seen fit to make the process work. Evolution itself presupposes the existence of some eternal reality which remains unchanged, and if we picture the gradual evolution of the cosmos, or the totality of physical reality, as modern science does, we demand a supra-physical, eternal, and therefore unchanging reality—or else there is no measure of change. Furthermore, this necessity remains, whatever method we may ultimately discover to have controlled the process of evolution.

The reader who is sceptical of the truth of evolution would do well to consult Canon Dorlodot's book, so often quoted in these pages, and see how he labors, not to prove that evolution is true, but to show how it is possible to hold a theory of less complete natural evolution than that held by the Fathers (because modern scientific evidence does not indicate that their view is possible) and still remain true to the principle of Catholic Naturalism which forbids calling on direct action by God when it is consistent with reason to explain a phenomenon by secondary causes.

It is also very important to bear in mind, in this connection, that the many able minds which have investigated this problem have been led to conclude that evolution is true, and it is not consonant with our ideas of God to suppose that He would construct nature so as to give a totally erroneous idea of its workings. As we pointed out before, God reveals Himself to man in the natural order as well as in the supernatural order and, if this order indicates that organisms appeared successively by descent from pre-existing forms, it is indeed rash to close our eyes to the evidence. The argument for evolution is a legitimate, incomplete induction which, as Dorlodot also points out, is exactly the kind of evidence which makes faith in revelation acceptable to the reasonable mind.

Evolution is not opposed to Catholicism. It is a scientific problem which can only be solved by scientific means and its metaphysical background was firmly established long ages before the scientific evidence was brought forward. Materialism is a philosophical explanation of the universe which has nothing in common with evolution.

The attempt to make evolution uphold materialism by claiming that it banished teleology or purposiveness never got very far. Certainly evolution does away with the idea that each particular organ was specially created for a particular type of organism in order to fulfill a particular purpose. That is the crude teleology which Thomas Huxley decried—though he went on to write, "But perhaps the most remarkable service to the philosophy of biology rendered by Mr. Darwin is the reconciliation of Teleology and Morphology, and the explanation of the facts of both which his views offer." [5] Charles Darwin's son wrote almost exactly the same thing concerning his father's work.

The evolution concept has changed the old *Argument for Design* as set forth by Paley in his *Evidences,* but it has not weakened it. Sir Bertram Windle wrote: "The argument is no longer one from the artifice to the artificer but from the artifice through the law by which it has constructed itself to the Lawgiver." [6] Even the avowed monist, Professor Plate of Berlin, maintained that, if there are laws of nature by means of which things work, there must be a Lawgiver.

The time has passed when anyone was justified in believing that evolution necessarily led to materialism, yet the real evil which has resulted from the concept is exactly along those lines and it results from the application of this supposed scientific fact to political systems and to human history. Unfortunately Darwin gave impetus to this when he wrote: "Hence we may look with some confidence to a secure future of great length. And as natural selection works solely by and for the good of each being, all corporeal and mental endowments will tend to progress towards perfection." [7] The confusion introduced here is evident if we recall that Natural Selection meant to Darwin the lopping off of the less-fit chance-variations by an impersonal environment; yet he employed such teleological terms

[5] *Darwiniana,* 1896, p. 110.
[6] *A Century of Scientific Thought,* 1915, p. 30.
[7] *Origin of Species,* Ch. XXV.

as good, selection, progress, perfection, and the application of the idea of necessary progress has been one of the most disastrous legacies of evolution. The devotees of "progress" have had their day, and that false notion has given way to scepticism or, in extreme cases, to absolute despair of man's future which is just as dangerous because it is equally far from the truth. Man *can* progress towards perfection but only by his own efforts, guided by the moral law, but just because he can progress, because there is a right which he can *choose* to do, he can retrogress by ignoring the *right* and choosing the *wrong*. A full realization of this fact and a willingness on the part of a majority of individuals to live accordingly, is the hope for man's future. For man is a reasonable being who possesses free will and the laws according to which the evolution of the purely material world has run its course are second in importance to his spiritual nature. It is useless for him to believe that he will improve without effort because of a natural law of evolution or development, and fatal for him to relax that effort, for he must either improve or retrogress morally—he cannot stand still.

Physical man certainly appears to be one with the rest of material creation. We know that he is formed from earth, from the same elements that compose the universe as a whole, and we know that his structure and blood are very similar to those of the rest of the mammals, more particularly to the apes. St. George Mivart (1827–1900), an important biologist and evolutionist, pointed out in his *Genesis of Species* that it was not necessary to believe that man's body was produced in a way different from those of the rest of the animals. This raised a storm of criticism and many Catholic theologians confidently expected him to be branded as a heretic by the Pope. But Pope Piux IX conferred on him the degree of Doctor of Philosophy and Cardinal Manning made the presentation at a public ceremony.[8]

No scientist claims that man has descended from the apes any more than any human being can be said to be descended from his twentieth cousin, but scientists are seeking to trace man's ancestry along the same lines as those of the animals that are structurally most similar to him and that appear, according to all known criteria, to be most closely related to him. The poverty of the fossil record makes this extremely difficult, and the careful, conscientious student is forced to acknowledge that we do not know much about man before the Paleolithic or Old Stone Age. Cro-Magnon man of Europe, the first who is definitely ascribed to the human species, *homo sapiens,* was as fully developed mentally and physically as modern man. The succeeding cultures spread from various centers and existed side by side with more primitive cultures just as they do today. It is certain now that within a few millennia of the first appearance of a real culture, man had developed a complex, civilized society which has advanced more rap-

[8] See article on St. George Mivart in *Catholic Encyclopedia* for the reasons that led to his later condemnation by Church authorities. Mivart, an evolutionist, took a stand opposed to Darwin, and Darwin, in turn, took great pains to answer his criticisms in detail. At that time Mivart was both a respected scientist and a Catholic.

idly in some places than in others and has undergone subsequent developments and retrogressions.

We cannot look too deeply here into the evidence for man's existence before Paleolithic times. There exist scattered fossil remains of human and possibly pre-human types and these are certainly of very great importance, but it is difficult to date them accurately and their exact significance is hard to establish. True man appears, in some instances, to antedate the supposedly sub-human types and it seems best, at present, to leave the whole question of man's lineage and the length of time which he has existed on the Earth for future decision after more facts have been established. The important thing is to realize that most of what we know about early man comes from the things he made and the acts he performed. Before we know him at all he had harnessed fire. Far back in the early stages of the Great Ice Age he picked up stones whose shapes made them useful and he chipped them crudely to increase their value. Before the middle of that period he had learned to shape tools for specific purposes. These things show that he was already man, with a mind capable of forming general concepts and was therefore distinct from the animals.

In favor of the idea of the evolution of man's body we have the well attested fact of the slow development of life from simple beginnings to the complex present-day creatures and, in view of the physical similarity of man to the animals, it is very difficult to break the chain at that point, for there are many other gaps as big or bigger in the long line of animal evolution. We also have, as mentioned before, scattered fossil remains of manlike creatures. These are not plentiful but, in the natural course of events, they will be increased by new finds. Their meaning, and man's true lineage, are still things for experts to dispute among themselves, but important as the whole subject is, it does not matter from the point of view of the Church's attitude toward man.

Catholics have been and continue to be in the forefront of anthropological studies. They are urged to be leaders in this as in other scientific pursuits. The proof of man's animal ancestry is growing stronger and the Church stands ready to accept it when the final word is in. In this case, as in the whole question of evolution, the Church's only care is to see that men do not twist a scientific fact into an evidence for materialism; that they do not make the discovery of a process the reason for denying the Mind behind the process and claim that, because man's body has evolved from the elements that compose the rocks, he has no higher destiny than have the rocks themselves or the lichens that cling to them.

The evolution of man's body can have no bearing on his supra-physical side. He shows his kinship with the material universe in many ways and it is not important in this connection whether God fashioned him separately after the plan of the higher animals or whether he drew him out, as it were, from the slime, through long ages of evolving animal creatures. We need not elaborate the real difference between man and the animals again. It has elsewhere been explained why we must regard man as partly spiritual if we are to form an adequate picture of him, and that is where the difference lies. The point is that God endowed man with a soul and so raised him to a higher plane and made him responsible for his actions.

CONCLUSION

RELIGION and science must work hand in hand if man is to reach his full development on this Earth. Each has its allotted place in a complete scheme of knowledge, and such a place is distinct enough so that each can make trouble by overstepping those bounds. Religion is based upon revelation, science depends upon observation of the material world, but both require the use of all the powers of man's mind and cannot be set aside in water-tight compartments. It is true that revelation, because of its origin, is knowledge that man could not have acquired in any other way, but the complete distinction ends there. Religion gives meaning to science, and science, in its turn, shows how God has chosen to construct the order of nature. Man, because he is a compound of body and soul, cannot devote his spiritual half to the practice of religion and preserve his material part for secular studies. He must give all of himself to everything that he does, and, at the same time, he must preserve a balance between those acts which bring him chiefly material benefits and those which pertain to the supernatural order.

It is because this balance is so hard to maintain and because man, immersed in a material environment, so easily overlooks his immaterial self, that the world is faced today with appalling dangers. For man, through his science, has tried to develop his material well being almost to the exclusion of his spiritual growth. He has made temporal gains paramount and now finds that the conquest of nature, which should benefit him so greatly, is more easily used for his own destruction or as an excuse for denying his dependence on God.

It appears inevitable to us that this single emphasis on the material development of a spiritual-material being *must* lead through ever-increasing difficulties to ultimate collapse. With the measure of right and wrong forgotten, with the justification for laws denied, there is little wonder that materialistic economics and sociology are incapable of revivifying civilization. As Father Philip Hughes writes: "Very simply the root of it all is man's apostasy from God. 'They that have forsaken the Lord shall be consumed; said the prophet' (Isaiah 1, 28), and man has not so much forsaken God as, to the best of his ability, he has banished Him for the life of this world. God's will is no longer a factor in the public life of the nations. Laws are made and administered, treaties arranged without even the form of a discussion as to their accordance with the will of God. The Divine thus banished, there disappears the chief reason why man should obey, the chief justification for a government's claim to command." [1]

Pope Pius XI set the correction of this evil as the prime purpose of his pontificate. He called upon the Catholic laity of the world to unite in order to help

[1] Philip Hughes, *Pope Pius the Eleventh,* N. Y., 1937, pp. 111–112.

bring the world back to a realization of its dependence on God. He defined the problem and indicated the means by which it may be solved, so that all who believe in Christian principles, all who accept the spiritual destiny of man and respect the rights of the individual, can unite with the Catholic Church in the effort to restore man to knowledge of the truth about himself.

We hear much about Catholic Action and should realize more fully what it means. It is, first of all, a call to knowledge; a demand that we be instructed and prepared as individuals to spread the truth. The Pope has said that ignorance of the Faith is the enemy which is most to be feared, and he lays it as a duty upon each of us to know our Faith and its deeper relations to philosophy. Realizing this, the Catholic laity cannot stand idly by, accepting material benefits while the world turns away from God, and expect its own spiritual life to remain unscathed. We cannot avoid the responsibility in view of the Pope's declaration that we *must* take an active part in "sharing the apostolic mission of the hierarchy." Therefore, we must be willing to work, and when that work has brought us knowledge, we must be prepared to present it to our fellow men.

Science covers a large field and many more workers are required to fill it. There is great need, moreover, of religious men, philosophically minded, who are likewise disciplined in some particular science so that they can be among the leaders in their chosen field. Christianity has been fighting a rear-guard action for too long. It has not surrendered, but it has been forever beating off the invader and defending its fundamentals from the inroads made by materialistic principles already proposed and already partly accepted. It is time for it to carry its own principles into the field of action before men have mistakenly chosen others. We need, in other words, more Catholic scientists and more lay Catholic philosophers who can prove that Catholicism and science are not only compatible, but that Catholic thinkers know how to avoid the materialistic errors which, like the evil things out of Pandora's box, have been loosed on the world and bid fair to destroy it.

We end with a plea to all Catholics who have any opportunity for education that they *make* themselves aware of the fundamental character of the struggle which lies before them; that they learn the broad principles of their faith so that each may help to guide the world towards God—the ultimate source of truth.

BIBLIOGRAPHICAL NOTE

THE references cited herein have been chosen from works in English or translations into English which are readily accessible. A complete list of authorities is, of course, out of the question, but any student wishing to read further need only follow up the references in the books listed.

There are no works known to the author which cover exactly the field of the present volume. The nearest approaches are Sir Bertram Windle's *The Church and Science* (St. Louis, 1917), and Rev. J. A. Zahm's *Bible, Science and Faith* (Baltimore 1895). They are both storehouses of valuable material and should be readily available for consultation. Two other books of a different sort, namely Andrew D. White's *A History of the Warfare of Science with Theology in Christendom,* and John W. Draper's *History of the Conflict between Religion and Science* (both New York, 1897 and in more recent editions) should be read by serious students after they have acquired sufficient knowledge to recognize the many errors in fact and interpretation in those volumes. They are classic examples of nineteenth century science's anti-Christian bias and their continued sale explains why so much misinformation is still abroad.

Henry Fairfield Osborne's *From the Greeks to Darwin* (New York, 1908), Henry S. Williams' *A History of Science* (5 vols., New York, 1904), and William Dampier-Whetham's *A History of Science and its Relations with Philosophy and Religion* (New York, 1929) present a summary of science from the earliest days to modern times. They are all written by non-Catholic scientists and are rela-

tively free from anti-Christian bias. Canon Henri de Dorlodot's *Darwinism and Catholic Thought* (translated into
English, New York, 1923) is the best authority for the
teachings of the Fathers in early Christian days. Sir Bertram Windle's *The Church and Science* and Rev. J. A.
Zahm's *Bible, Science and Faith* (both noted above) discuss the first chapter of Genesis in all its relations to science,
and John A. O'Brien's *Evolution and Religion* (New York,
1932) considers the general topic of science and biblical
interpretation.

Medieval science is also discussed in the books just
noted but the most exhaustive treatment is in Lynn Thorndike's *History of Magic and Experimental Science* (4 vols.,
New York 1923–1934). Vol. 2 deals particularly with
Roger Bacon, St. Albertus Magnus, St. Thomas Aquinas,
their contemporaries and immediate successors. The same
author's *Science and Thought in the Fifteenth Century*
(New York, 1929) deals comprehensively with the science
of the late Middle Ages, and Dr. James J. Walsh's *The
Popes and Science* (New York, 1908) is devoted particularly to the medicine and surgery of those times.

The best reference material for the controversies over
the form of the Earth, the existence of antipodeans, Noah's
deluge, and fossils, will be found in the works by Rev. J. A.
Zahm and Sir Bertram Windle referred to above. A quotation from Rev. E. R. Hull, S. J., on pages 54–55 of *The
Church and Science* presents a clear statement of the
Church's attitude towards controversial scientific hypothe-
ses. Sir Archibald Geikie's *The Founders of Geology*
(New York, 1905) summarizes many of the early ideas
about fossils and some other aspects of Greek and Roman
science. The essay on Nicholas Stensen by Sir Bertram
Windle in *Twelve Catholic Men of Science* (Edited by
Windle, London, 1923) is the best brief biography of that
remarkable man and shows his importance to science, par-

ticularly to geology. A brief outline of his career and geological doctrines can also be found in *The Founders of Geology* (see above).

The supposed Papal prohibitions of surgery and chemistry are refuted by fully documented discussions in Dr. Walsh's *The Popes and Science*. Lynn Thorndike's *Science and Thought in the Fifteenth Century* also presents much material on the same subject.

The controversy over Copernican astronomy, centering about the person of Galileo is briefly but thoroughly discussed by Rev. E. R. Hull, S.J. in *Galileo and His Condemnation* (London, 1923). John A. O'Brien's *Evolution and Religion,* Sir Bertram Windle's *The Church and Science* (particularly pp. 25–32), and the article on Galileo in the *Catholic Encyclopedia* refer to Father Hull's work and state all that need be known concerning the matter.

There are no complete summaries of the problems concerning evolution. It is a living issue which has spread from science to philosophy, history, and sociology. The best recent works of apologetics on this question are John A. O'Brien's *Evolution and Religion,* and Henri de Dorlodot's *Darwinism and Catholic Thought* both of which have previously been noted in other connections. These works, together with Rev. J. A. Zahm's *Evolution and Dogma* (Chicago, 1896), Rev. Joseph Husslein's *Evolution and Social Progress* (New York, 1920), *The Problem of Evolution* by Rev. Eric Wasmann, S.J. (St. Louis, 1912), *A Century of Scientific Thought* by Sir Bertram Windle (London, 1915), and *The Church and Science* by the same author should forever dispel the illusion that the Church is opposed to evolution.

The Theory of Evolution, by Professor William B. Scott (New York, 1919) is an excellent brief discussion of the evidences and meaning of evolution. *New Views of Evolution,* by Professor C. P. Conger (New York, 1929) also considers the evidence and distinguishes clearly between proof and probability. *Evolution, Genetics and Eugenics* by Professor H. H. Newman (Chicago, Rev. Ed. 1925) is an authoritative work which discusses the various theories of evolution as well as the evidence. Dr. Herbert F. Standing's *Spirit in Evolution* (New York, 1930), written for the general reader, shows that an evolutionist need not be a materialist. Professor Richard S. Lull's *Organic Evolution* (New York, 1917) is another valuable general survey of the problem.

Naturally, the best way to appreciate the work which Darwin accomplished is to read both his *Origin of Species* and *Descent of Man,* and supplement this with Thomas Huxley's *Darwiniana* and Francis Darwin's *Life and Letters of Charles Darwin.* All of these may be obtained in numerous editions.

Finally, the student who wishes to realize the extent and value of the work of Catholic scientists should consult Rev. J. A. Zahm's *Catholic Science and Catholic Scientists* (St. Louis, 1894), *Twelve Catholic Men of Science,* Ed. by Sir Bertram Windle (London, 1923), Dr. James J. Walsh's *Catholic Churchmen in Science* (3 vols., Philadelphia, 1917), and Edward J. Menge's *The Beginnings of Science* (Boston, 1918).

ABSTRACT FOR STUDY AND REVIEW

I

The Development of Science

A general idea of the history of science and of the scientific method is essential in order to understand the controversies between science and religion.

1. Practical science originated in the prehistoric period but the Greeks were the first to place scientific knowledge on a rational basis (500 B.C. to 400 B.C.). Roman genius inclined to other things so that scientific advances during the Roman ascendency were made by men of other nationalities. Also, late pagan science was thoroughly mixed with magic and this was handed down as a legacy to the early Christians.

2. Early Christian times witnessed a further influx of mysticism from the East, consequently Christian teachers were immediately obliged to distinguish between Christ's miracles and popular magic. It was an age of learning, however, and the Fathers were forced to justify their faith in terms acceptable to educated men. St. Gregory of Nyssa and St. Augustine were the leaders in developing Christian Cosmology and establishing the concept of Catholic Naturalism.

3. When Rome collapsed the spread, even the retention, of learning became difficult. Science nearly disappeared in Europe but was later re-introduced from Arabian sources. Little is known about science in the early Middle Ages but the resurgence of science at the time of Roger Bacon and St. Albertus Magnus proves that the groundwork had al-

ready been laid. The Middle Ages, however, must not be thought of as a scientific period, although alchemy and astrology flourished.

4. As scholasticism deteriorated it ceased to incorporate new ideas, but the rapid development of science from the sixteenth century on shows that the seeds had been present all the time and that rigorous scholastic logic had prepared the way for its growth.

5. The new science drew away from the old philosophy because the majority of men of that period, being unaccustomed to new ideas, would not accept them. Theologians were partially responsible for this but the existing science was just as antagonistic to new modes of thought. Science, lacking a philosophic basis, developed a materialistic bias, and controversies arose. These were due to mistakes made on both sides and similar ones can only be avoided in the future by patience and mutual understanding.

II

Controversies about Geography and Astronomy

Some of the early controversies between the Church and the science of the day concerned the form of the Earth, the distribution of its inhabitants, and the relation of the Earth to the other celestial bodies.

1. The Greek scientists knew that the Earth was spheroidal. The common view then and in the Middle Ages was, however, that the Earth was flat and that all its inhabitants were on one side. Christian apologists never did oppose the idea that the Earth was a sphere. Nevertheless, some did contest the notion that men might live on the other side. They did this because they could not see how descendants of Adam could cross the barriers of water or, even if they had, how they could have been saved by Christ.

They labored to uphold the unity of the human race but were wrong in assuming that they knew enough about it to justify their passing judgment on the matter.

2. The famous controversy over Copernican astronomy should be divided into two parts (a) Copernicus published his *Revolution of the Heavenly Bodies* at the request of one Pope, but only after repeated urging by two Bishops, and dedicated it to another Pope. A friend introduced a preface saying that Copernicus' views were purely hypothetical. The whole idea was ill received by mathematicians and astronomers, was rejected by the Protestant sects, but was little noticed by the Catholic Church. (b) When it was discovered that Copernicus had believed that what he wrote was true, the Catholic Church raised objections. Galileo was converted to Copernicism and entered the controversy when he began to teach it as a fact. He was stopped and made to retract and promise not to teach it. He later broke his word and was once more made to retract. Copernicus' work was placed on the Index and many years passed before this prohibition was removed. Many erroneous statements have been made concerning the Church's attitude and actions in this case but, at best, a serious error (one, however, which does not involve infallibility) must be admitted.

III

Controversies about Geology and Some Imaginary Controversies

1. The controversy over the meaning of fossils hinges on the idea that the Church could not allow men to recognize their true significance without giving up her long established chronology. This is easily refuted by pointing out that the Church has never pronounced on the question

107

of biblical chronology and that innumerable Catholics could and did study the matter, teach what fossils were, and show what their existence indicated.

2. The controversy over Noah's flood proves the Church's readiness to recognize scientific facts. In the early days there was little reason to question the apparent meaning of the biblical account. When geology developed sufficiently to show the impossibility of the old view the Church reopened the matter of interpretation.

3. The Church has been accused of retarding the development of medicine by refusing to allow dissection of the human body. This idea is based on misinterpretation of a Papal decree and it, again, can best be refuted by citing some of the history of medicine and showing that the best of the early medical work was done in Italy under the patronage of the Popes.

IV

Organic Evolution

1. Evolution and special creation are two possible ways of explaining the great variety of organisms. Evolution is the process which science believes operated to bring this about. It is a scientific problem and should not be confused with materialism or other philosophies. The idea of evolution goes back to Aristotle and was strongly supported by the Christian Fathers. St. Thomas Aquinas introduced certain changes but no really scientific study of the problem was undertaken until the time of Lamarck at the end of the eighteenth century. It was not accepted until Darwin's evidence was presented to the world.

V

Evidences of Evolution and Recent Trends in Biological Science

1. The evidences of evolution come from such diverse things as studies of animals under domestication, comparative anatomy, embryology, blood tests, paleontology, and the distribution of living things. The evidence gains in strength because of this convergence from many sources.

2. Theories of how evolution came about must not be confused with the process itself. The latter is firmly established in science but no explanation or combination of explanations is satisfactory today. Lamarck's theory of use and disuse, Darwin's natural selection, Weissman's distinction between body and germ cells, DeVries' emphasis on mutations, and Mendel's genetic experiments have all contributed to our understanding of the problem. The latter is particularly important since it indicates the mechanism of heredity, but the means whereby changes originate remain obscure.

3. The Catholic in particular must hesitate to decry evolution or be fooled into accepting certain explanations of evolution as less materialistic than others. Such acceptance implies a knowledge of how God has worked which we have no right to claim.

Many hold that scientific evidence indicates man's descent from animal ancestry, that the problem is a complex one and that there is no basis either in revelation or Scripture for judging the matter. According to them the question must be determined on the basis of evidence yet to be discovered. In either case God created man and, also in either case, God distinguished him from brute creation by the gift of a soul.